# AT THE BREAKING OF THE BREAD

## The Methodist Worship Book
## Communion Services
## Illustrated Edition

*At the Breaking of the Bread* paperback edition ISBN 1 85852 208 0
casebound edition ISBN 1 85852 209 9

© 2001 Trustees for Methodist Church Purposes
Illustrations © Turvey Abbey

First published as *The Methodist Worship Book* 1999.

This edition first published June 2001.

*The Methodist Worship Book* is available in the following editions:

Standard full text, English, ISBN 1 85852 116 5

Presentation Editions, full text

      Bound in Blue, ISBN 1 85852 119 X
      Bound in Red, ISBN 1 85852 120 3
      Bound in Green, ISBN 1 85852 121 1

additionally there is a

      Large Print Edition (printed in black only), ISBN 1 85852 118 1

and a

      Bilingual English/Welsh edition, ISBN 1 85852 117 3

Also available, as sections, are:

      Admission, Commissioning and Welcome Services, ISBN 1 85852 137 8
      Baptism of Young Children, ISBN 1 85852 130 0
      The Covenant Service, ISBN 1 85852 133 5
      Daily Prayer, ISBN 1 85852 136 X
      Entry into the Church, ISBN 1 85852 131 9
      Funeral, ISBN 1 85852 135 1
      Holy Communion Services, ISBN 1 85852 132 7
      Marriage and Blessing, ISBN 1 85852 134 3

Printed in Great Britain by Stanley L. Hunt (Printers) Limited, Midland Road, Rushden, Northamptonshire NN10 9UA.

# CONTENTS

## Thanks

The publishers wish to acknowledge their gratitude to:

The Sisters of the Order of Saint Benedict, Turvey Abbey for the illustrations
Judy Jarvis and the staff of the Children's Section of the Methodist Church Team
Susan Gascoigne who set the text
Lorna Lackenby for the graphic design

# ORDERS OF SERVICE FOR HOLY COMMUNION

## Introduction

Holy Communion, or the Lord's Supper, is the central act of Christian worship, in which the Church responds to our Lord's command, 'Do this in remembrance of me' (1 Corinthians 11:24-25).

Many of the themes of John and Charles Wesley's **Hymns on the Lord's Supper** (1745) are reflected in present-day ecumenical understanding of this sacrament. In communion with the people of God in heaven and on earth, we give thanks for God's mighty acts in creation and redemption, represented supremely in the life, death and resurrection of Jesus Christ. In this means of grace, the Church joyfully celebrates the presence of Christ in its midst, calls to mind his sacrifice and, in the power of the Holy Spirit, is united with him as the Body of Christ. At the Lord's table, Christ's disciples share bread and wine, the tokens of his dying love and the food for their earthly pilgrimage, which are also a foretaste of the heavenly banquet, prepared for all people. Those who gather around the table of the Lord are empowered for mission: apostles, sent out in the power of the Spirit, to live and work to God's praise and glory. One of the keynotes of the Methodist revival was John Wesley's emphasis on 'The Duty of Constant Communion' and it is still the duty and privilege of members of the Methodist Church to share in this sacrament. The Methodist Conference has encouraged local churches to admit baptized children to communion. Those who are communicants and belong to other Churches whose discipline so permits are also welcome as communicants in the Methodist Church.

The services of *Holy Communion* in this book are set out, after the initial 'The Gathering of the People of God', under the two historic headings, 'The Ministry of the Word' and 'The Lord's Supper'. The hinge point between the two is normally the sharing of the Peace. The shape of the Lord's Supper follows the record in scripture of Jesus' characteristic sharing with his disciples, especially after the final meal on the night before the crucifixion. His seven actions with the bread and wine (four with the bread, three with the wine) were taken up in the Church's tradition as a fourfold shape: Taking, Giving Thanks, Breaking and Sharing. In the Great Thanksgiving, the service of praise offered by God's people on earth is joined with the praises of the heavenly host, praising God, Father, Son and Holy Spirit. This Eucharistic Prayer (the word 'Eucharist', derived from a Greek word which means 'Thanksgiving', is increasingly accepted by Christians of all traditions as one of the names for this sacrament) is Trinitarian both in its structure and in its focus.

In this book, complete orders for *Holy Communion* have been provided for the major festivals and seasons, offering a wide range of seasonal language and imagery throughout each service. This also has the practical advantage that each service is complete in itself so that there is no need to turn to different parts of the book to find additional material. There are three orders for use in Ordinary Seasons (that is, when it is not a particular season or festival). Other sections of **The Methodist Worship Book** provide eucharistic prayers for certain specific occasions.

# Notes

1    The basic elements of each service are marked by either a bold blue number or bold blue text, eg **1** or **Either two or three . . . .** Other sections may be omitted.

2    The following services and sections which appear in other editions of **The Methodist Worship Book** have been omitted from this version.

> Holy Communion for Ash Wednesday (or the First Sunday in Lent)
> Guidance for Ordering a Service of Holy Communion
> Holy Communion in a Home or Hospital
> Extended Communion

3    The term 'presiding minister' in these services means a presbyter or a person with an authorisation from the Conference to preside at the Lord's Supper. The presiding minister should begin and end the service. She/he should also greet the people at the Peace and preside over the fourfold Eucharistic action by taking the bread and wine, leading the Great Prayer of Thanksgiving, breaking the bread, and presiding over the sharing of the bread and wine. Other people may be invited to share in other parts of the service.

4    In some churches it is customary to stand for the reading of the Gospel.

5    The juice of the grape shall be used.

6    What remains of the elements should be reverently consumed, or otherwise reverently disposed of, at the end of the service.

7    The following notes apply to particular services or groups of services:

**Advent**
An Advent ceremony, such as the lighting of Advent candles, may be included after either no. 1 or no. 7, or at some other appropriate place.

**Christmas and Epiphany**
This service is intended for use between midnight on Christmas Eve and the Sunday after Epiphany inclusive.

**Ordinary Seasons**
These services are intended for use (1) in the period which follows the Sunday after Epiphany and precedes Ash Wednesday and (2) in the period which follows the Day of Pentecost and precedes the First Sunday of Advent. In the Second Service, musical settings other than those printed may be used.

# Advent, Christmas and Epiphany

## *We come together*

## Advent

THE GATHERING OF THE PEOPLE OF GOD

**1** The presiding minister says:

Grace and peace to you
from God our Father and the Lord
 Jesus Christ.
Blessèd are those who will come
from east and west, from north and south,
to feast in the kingdom of God.

2 Hymn

3 God of all glory,
you brought the universe into existence,
and raised up witnesses
to your greatness and love.
We praise and adore you.
Grant that by the inspiration of your
 Holy Spirit
we may worship and serve you,
and praise your holy name;
through Christ our Lord. **Amen.**

## Christmas and Epiphany

THE GATHERING OF THE PEOPLE OF GOD

**1** The presiding minister says:

Great and wonderful are the things
the Lord our God has done for us.
The people who walked in darkness
have seen a great light.

2 Hymn

3 In the silence and stillness
let us open our hearts and lives to God,
that we may be prepared for his coming
as Light and Word, as Bread and Wine.

Silence

**4** The commandments of the Lord Jesus may be read.

Our Lord Jesus Christ said: 'The first commandment is, "Hear, O Israel: the Lord our God, the Lord is one; you shall love the Lord your God with all your heart, and with all your soul, and with all your mind, and with all your strength." The second is this, "You shall love your neighbour as yourself." There is no other commandment greater than these.' 'I give you a new commandment, that you love one another. Just as I have loved you, you also should love one another.'

**Amen. Lord, have mercy.**

**5** The presiding minister says:

Let us confess our sins to God, trusting in his mercy and forgiveness.

**Holy and forgiving God,**
**we have sinned against you and each other**
**in thought and word and deed.**
**We have turned from your life-giving word,**
**and ignored the message of those you sent.**
**We are unprepared for the coming of your**
**    Son.**
**Have mercy upon us and forgive us,**
**that strengthened by your love**
**we may serve you more faithfully;**
**through Jesus Christ our Lord. Amen.**

Silence

'I am making all things new,' says the Lord.

This is Christ's gracious word:

'Your sins are forgiven.'

**Amen. Thanks be to God.**

**4** The presiding minister says:

We say together:

**Loving God,**
**you have searched us and known us,**
**our blindness, our frailties,**
**our fears and our selfishness.**
**In sorrow we confess**
**that we have sinned against you**
**and disobeyed your command to love.**
**Forgive us,**
**for the sake of your Son, Jesus Christ,**
**who became like us**
**that we might become like him. Amen.**

The true light that gives light to everyone has come into the world.
To all who receive him,
he gives power to become children of God.
This is Christ's gracious word:

'Your sins are forgiven.'

**Amen. Thanks be to God.**

**6** The collect of the day, or this or some other prayer:

> God of mercy and power,
> whose Son rules over all,
> grant us so to live in obedience to your holy
>   will,
> that at his appearing
> we may be raised to eternal life;
> through Jesus Christ our Lord.  **Amen.**

The collect of the Advent season which appears on page 523 of other editions may also be used.

7 Hymn

OR *Benedictus*

Blessèd be the Lord, the God of Israel,
who has come to his people and set them free.

**The Lord has raised up for us a mighty**
**  Saviour,**
**born of the house of his servant David.**

Through the holy prophets, God promised
  of old
to save us from our enemies,
from the hands of all who hate us,
to show mercy to our forebears,
and to remember his holy covenant.

**This was the oath God swore to our father**
**  Abraham:**
**to set us free from the hands of our enemies,**
**free to worship him without fear,**
**holy and righteous before him,**
**all the days of our life.**

And you, child, shall be called the prophet
  of the Most High,

**5** The collect of the day, or this or some other prayer:

> Ever-living God,
> whose glory was revealed
> in the Word made flesh,
> may we, who have seen such splendour
> in the coming of your Son,
> be true witnesses to your self-giving love in
>   the world;
> through Jesus Christ our Lord,
> who is alive and reigns with you,
> in the unity of the Holy Spirit,
> one God, now and for ever.  **Amen.**

6 EITHER *Glory to God in the highest*

**Glory to God in the highest,**
**and peace to God's people on earth.**

**Lord God, heavenly King,**
**almighty God and Father,**
**we worship you, we give you thanks,**
**we praise you for your glory.**

**Lord Jesus Christ, only Son of the Father,**
**Lord God, Lamb of God,**
**you take away the sin of the world:**
**have mercy on us;**
**you are seated at the right hand of the**
**  Father:**
**receive our prayer.**

**For you alone are the Holy One,**
**you alone are the Lord,**
**you alone are the Most High, Jesus Christ,**
**with the Holy Spirit,**
**in the glory of God the Father.  Amen.**

for you will go before the Lord to prepare
  his way,
to give his people knowledge of salvation
by the forgiveness of their sins.

**In the tender compassion of our God
the dawn from heaven shall break upon us,
to shine on those who dwell in darkness and
  the shadow of death,
and to guide our feet into the way of peace.**

Glory to the Father, and to the Son,
and to the Holy Spirit:
**as it was in the beginning, is now,
and shall be for ever.  Amen.**

OR *Magnificat*

My soul proclaims the greatness of the Lord,
my spirit rejoices in God my Saviour,
who has looked with favour on his lowly
  servant.

**From this day all generations will call me
  blessèd:
the Almighty has done great things for me
and holy is his name.**

OR *A Song of the Incarnation*

**The grace of God has dawned upon the
  world
with healing for all.
The people who walked in darkness
have seen a great light:
Light has dawned upon us,
dwellers in a land as dark as death.
For a child has been born for us,
a son given to us.**

**God is love;
and his love was disclosed to us in this,
that he sent his only Son into the world to
  bring us life.
We know how generous our Lord Jesus
  Christ has been:
he was rich, yet for our sake he became poor,
so that through his poverty we might
  become rich.**

God has mercy on those who fear him,
from generation to generation.

**The Lord has shown strength with his arm
and scattered the proud in their conceit,
casting down the mighty from their thrones
and lifting up the lowly.**

God has filled the hungry with good things
and sent the rich away empty.

**He has come to the aid of his servant Israel,
to remember the promise of mercy,
the promise made to our forebears,
to Abraham and his children for ever.**

Glory to the Father, and to the Son,
and to the Holy Spirit:
**as it was in the beginning, is now,
and shall be for ever.  Amen.**

**God has spoken to us in the Son
whom he has made heir to the whole
  universe.
The Word became flesh and came to dwell
  among us.
We saw his glory,
such glory as befits the Father's only Son,
full of grace and truth.**

## THE MINISTRY OF THE WORD

**Either two or three readings from scripture follow, the last of which is the Gospel.**

8  Old Testament reading

9  A Psalm or portion of a Psalm may be said or sung.

10  Epistle

11  Hymn

12  A reading from the Gospel according to . . .

Hear the Gospel of Christ.
**Glory to Christ our Saviour.**

The Gospel is read.

This is the Gospel of Christ.
**Praise to Christ our Lord.**

**13** Sermon

14  Hymn

## THE MINISTRY OF THE WORD

**Either two or three readings  from scripture follow, the last of which is the Gospel.**

7  Old Testament reading

8  A Psalm or portion of a Psalm may be said or sung.

9  Epistle

10  Hymn

11  A reading from the Gospel according to . . .

Hear the Gospel of Christ.
**Glory to Christ our Saviour.**

The Gospel is read.

This is the Gospel of Christ.
**Praise to Christ our Lord.**

**12** Sermon

13  Hymn

**15** These or some other prayers of intercession:

Let us pray.

In joyful expectation of his coming to reign
we pray to our Lord, saying,
Come, Lord Jesus.

**Come, Lord Jesus.**

Come to your world as King of
  the nations.
We pray for . . .
Before you rulers will stand in silence.
Come, Lord Jesus.

**Come, Lord Jesus.**

Come to your Church as Lord and Judge.
We pray for . . .
Help us to live in the light of your coming
and give us a longing to do your will.
Come, Lord Jesus.

**Come, Lord Jesus.**

**14** These or some other prayers of intercession:

Let us pray.

Unlooked for,
Christ comes.

To shepherds,
watching their sheep through the long, dark
  night,
he comes with the glory of the angels' song
and in the humility of the manger.

Silence

Loving God, we pray for our community . . .
In the midst of our everyday lives, surprise us
with glimpses of the glorious, humble love at
the heart of existence.

Lord, come to your people.
**In your mercy set us free.**

Searched for,
Christ comes.

To the wise and powerful,
star-led to Bethlehem, seeking a king,
he comes, child of Mary,

crowned with meekness,
worthy of every gift.

Silence

Loving God, we pray for the leaders of the
world . . .
Guide them with your light to the true
wisdom of justice and peace, of freedom and
respect for every human life.

Lord, come to your people.
**In your mercy set us free.**

Longed for,
Christ comes.

To Anna and Simeon,
whose days are lived in faithful expectation,
he comes, a new life to the old,
a living prophecy of hope.

Silence

Loving God, we pray for the Church in all the
world . . .
Unite us by your Spirit, and make us faithful
witnesses to the hope we have in you.

Lord, come to your people.
**In your mercy set us free.**

Come to your people
as Saviour and bearer of pain.
We pray for . . .
Enfold us all in your love and mercy,
wipe away the tears of failure, fear and
   distress,
and set us free to serve you for ever.
Come, Lord Jesus.

**Come, Lord Jesus.**

Come to us from heaven
with power and great glory,
and lift us up to meet you,
where with all your saints and angels,
we will live with you for ever.
Come, Lord Jesus.

**Come, Lord Jesus.  Amen.**

16  Silence

Prayed for,
Christ comes.

To men and women, girls and boys,
crying out in darkness, pain and loneliness,
he comes, baptized, at one with us,
our Saviour, healer and friend.

Silence

Loving God, we pray for those whose lives
are hard and painful or whose existence is
sorrowful, bitter or empty . . .
In their need, may they know your healing
touch, reaching out to comfort, strengthen
and restore.

Lord, come to your people.
**In your mercy set us free.**

Unlooked for and searched for,
longed for and prayed for,
loving God, you come to us now
as you have come to your people in every age.
We thank you for all who have reflected the
   light of Christ.
Help us to follow their example
and bring us with them to eternal life;
through Jesus Christ our Lord.  **Amen.**

15  The Lord's Prayer
EITHER

We say together the prayer that Jesus gave us:

**Our Father in heaven,
hallowed be your Name,
your kingdom come,
your will be done,
on earth as in heaven.
Give us today our daily bread.
Forgive us our sins
as we forgive those who sin against us.
Save us from the time of trial
and deliver us from evil.
For the kingdom, the power and
   the glory are yours,
now and for ever.  Amen.**

**17 EITHER**

Let us pray.

**We do not presume
to come to this your table, merciful Lord,
trusting in our own righteousness,
but in your manifold and great mercies.
We are not worthy
so much as to gather up the crumbs under
   your table.
But you are the same Lord
whose nature is always to have mercy.
Grant us therefore, gracious Lord,
so to eat the flesh of your dear Son
   Jesus Christ,
and to drink his blood,
that we may evermore dwell in him
and he in us. Amen.**

OR

As our Saviour taught his disciples, we pray:

**Our Father, who art in heaven,
hallowed be thy Name;
thy kingdom come;
thy will be done;
on earth as it is in heaven.
Give us this day our daily bread.
And forgive us our trespasses,
as we forgive those who trespass against us.
And lead us not into temptation;
but deliver us from evil.
For thine is the kingdom, the power,
   and the glory,
for ever and ever. Amen.**

OR

We say together:

**Lord, we come to your table,**
**trusting in your mercy**
**and not in any goodness of our own.**
**We are not worthy**
**even to gather up the crumbs under your**
**table,**
**but it is your nature always to have mercy,**
**and on that we depend.**
**So feed us with the body and blood**
**of Jesus Christ, your Son,**
**that we may for ever live in him**
**and he in us. Amen.**

18 The Peace

All stand.

May the God of peace make you holy
and keep you free from every fault
as you wait in joyful hope
for the coming of our Lord Jesus Christ.

The peace of the Lord be always with you.
**And also with you.**

The people may greet one another in the name
of Christ.

16 The Peace

All stand.

Glory to God in the highest,
and on earth peace to all in whom
he delights.

The peace of the Lord be always with you.
**And also with you.**

The people may greet one another in the name
of Christ.

GLORY TO GOD

## 17 The Nicene Creed

All stand.

Let us profess the faith of the Church.

We believe in one God,
the Father, the Almighty,
maker of heaven and earth,
of all that is, seen and unseen.

We believe in one Lord, Jesus Christ,
the only Son of God,
eternally begotten of the Father,
God from God, Light from Light,
true God from true God,
begotten, not made,
of one Being with the Father;
through him all things were made.
For us and for our salvation
he came down from heaven,
was incarnate of the Holy Spirit and the
 Virgin Mary
and became truly human.
For our sake he was crucified under
 Pontius Pilate;
he suffered death and was buried.

On the third day he rose again
in accordance with the Scriptures;
he ascended into heaven
and is seated at the right hand of the Father.
He will come again in glory to judge the
 living and the dead,
and his kingdom will have no end.

We believe in the Holy Spirit, the Lord, the
 giver of life,
who proceeds from the Father and the Son,
who with the Father and the Son is
 worshipped and glorified,
who has spoken through the prophets.
We believe in one holy catholic and
 apostolic Church.
We acknowledge one Baptism for the
 forgiveness of sins.
We look for the resurrection of the dead,
and the life of the world to come. Amen.

### THE PREPARATION OF THE GIFTS

**19** Hymn

**20** The offerings of the people are presented. Bread and wine are brought to the table (or if already on the table are uncovered). The presiding minister takes the bread and wine and prepares them for use.

### THE LORD'S SUPPER

### THE PREPARATION OF THE GIFTS

**18** Hymn

**19** The offerings of the people are presented. Bread and wine are brought to the table (or if already on the table are uncovered). The presiding minister takes the bread and wine and prepares them for use.

**20**    Lord and Giver of every good thing,
we bring to you
bread and wine for our communion,
lives and gifts for your kingdom,
all for transformation through your grace
  and love,
made known in Jesus Christ our Saviour.
**Amen.**

### THE THANKSGIVING

**21** All stand.

The presiding minister leads the great prayer of thanksgiving:

The Lord be with you.
**And also with you.**

Lift up your hearts.
**We lift them to the Lord.**

Let us give thanks to the Lord our God.
**It is right to give our thanks and praise.**

God of all glory and light of our salvation,
we offer you thanks and praise
through Jesus Christ your Son our Lord.

By your living Word
you called all things into being,
breathed into life the desire of your heart
and shaped us in your own likeness.
Though we rejected your love,
you did not give us up
or cease to fashion our salvation.
You made a covenant to be our God,
spoke to us through the prophets,
and prepared the way for our redemption.

### THE THANKSGIVING

**21** All stand.

The presiding minister leads the great prayer of thanksgiving:

The Lord be with you.
**And also with you.**

Lift up your hearts.
**We lift them to the Lord.**

Let us give thanks to the Lord our God.
**It is right to give our thanks and praise.**

Father, it is our joy and delight,
our reason for being,
to offer you thanks and praise.

All your actions show wisdom and love.
Through your Word you spoke creation into
  existence
and made us in your image and likeness.
When we disobeyed you and drew away
  from you,
you did not leave us in darkness

We praise you that in the fullness of time
you sent your only Son Jesus Christ.

The Lord of eternity,
announced by angels and born of Mary,
he became incarnate,
fulfilling the promise of your salvation.

And so we offer our praise
with all your people, on earth and in heaven.
With the full chorus of your creation,
we proclaim the glory of your name:

**Holy, holy, holy Lord,**
**God of power and might,**
**heaven and earth are full of your glory.**
**Hosanna in the highest.**
**Blessèd is he who comes in the name of the**
  **Lord.**
**Hosanna in the highest.**

We praise you, Lord God, King of the
  universe,
through our Lord Jesus Christ,
who, on the night in which he was betrayed,
took bread, gave thanks, broke it,
and gave it to his disciples, saying,
'Take this and eat it.
This is my body given for you.
Do this in remembrance of me.'

In the same way, after supper,
he took the cup, gave thanks,
and gave it to them, saying,
'Drink from it all of you.
This is my blood of the new covenant,
poured out for you and for many,
for the forgiveness of sins.
Do this, whenever you drink it,
in remembrance of me.'

**Christ has died.**
**Christ is risen.**
**Christ will come in glory.**
**He is Alpha and Omega,**
**the beginning and the end;**
**the King of kings, and Lord of lords.**

but sent your Son, the Word made flesh,
to be the light of the world.

Emptying himself of all but love,
he was born of Mary,
shared our human nature and died on the
  cross.

Yet you have raised him from death to
  eternal life;
and through him you have sent your holy and
  life-giving Spirit
to make us your people, a people of light,
to reflect your glory in all the earth.

And so with angels and archangels
and all the heavenly choir
we join in the unending hymn of praise:

**Holy, holy, holy Lord,**
**God of power and might,**
**heaven and earth are full of your glory.**
**Hosanna in the highest.**
**Blessèd is he who comes in the name of the**
  **Lord.**
**Hosanna in the highest.**

Holy and redeeming God,
we see your grace and truth in Jesus Christ
  our Lord,
who, on the night in which he was betrayed,
took bread, gave thanks, broke it,
and gave it to his disciples, saying,
'Take this and eat it.
This is my body given for you.
Do this in remembrance of me.'

In the same way, after supper,
he took the cup, gave thanks,
and gave it to them, saying,
'Drink from it all of you.
This is my blood of the new covenant,
poured out for you and for many,
for the forgiveness of sins.
Do this, whenever you drink it,
in remembrance of me.'

**Christ is born.**
**The Saviour has come.**
**God is with us.**

Recalling his death and resurrection,
and in obedience to his command,
we celebrate the offering of his eternal
   sacrifice,
until he comes again.

Through him, our Priest and King,
accept us as a living sacrifice,
a people for your praise.

Generous and holy God,
pour out your Spirit
that these gifts of bread and wine
may be for us the body and blood of Christ.

Refashion us in your image
that we may be found ready
at the coming of our Lord Jesus Christ.

**Blessing and honour and glory and power
be yours, O Lord, for ever and ever.  Amen.**

**22** The Lord's Prayer

EITHER

We say together the prayer that Jesus gave us:

**Our Father in heaven,
hallowed be your Name,
your kingdom come,
your will be done,
on earth as in heaven.
Give us today our daily bread.
Forgive us our sins
as we forgive those who sin against us.
Save us from the time of trial
and deliver us from evil.
For the kingdom, the power and
   the glory are yours,
now and for ever.  Amen.**

And so, Father, we remember and celebrate
all that Christ has done for us.

Send your Holy Spirit
that these gifts of bread and wine
may be for us the body and blood of Christ.

Through him we give ourselves to you.
May your Spirit draw us together
in the one body of Christ,
that we may have life in all its fullness,
live in your love,
and fill creation with a song of never-ending
   praise.

We ask this through your Son,
Jesus Christ our Lord.

**Through him, with him, and in him,
in the unity of the Holy Spirit,
all honour and glory be given to you,
almighty Father,
throughout all ages.  Amen.**

OR

As our Saviour taught his disciples, we pray:

**Our Father, who art in heaven,
hallowed be thy Name;
thy kingdom come;
thy will be done;
on earth as it is in heaven.
Give us this day our daily bread.
And forgive us our trespasses,
as we forgive those who trespass against us.
And lead us not into temptation;
but deliver us from evil.
For thine is the kingdom, the power,
  and the glory,
for ever and ever.  Amen.**

THE BREAKING OF THE BREAD

**23** The presiding minister breaks the bread in the sight of the people in silence, or saying:

The bread we break is a sharing in the body of Christ.

The cup we take is a sharing in the blood of Christ.

**Happy are those who share the banquet.**

OR

Like those that look for the morning so our souls wait for the Lord.

**Be known to us, Lord, in the breaking of the bread.**

**24** Silence, all seated or kneeling

THE BREAKING OF THE BREAD

**22** The presiding minister breaks the bread in the sight of the people in silence, or saying:

Christ is the Bread of Life.
Christ is the Light of the World.

**God here among us,
light in the midst of us,
bring us light and life.**

**23** Silence, all seated or kneeling

THE SHARING OF THE BREAD AND WINE

**25** The presiding minister, those assisting with the distribution, and the people receive, according to local custom.

The presiding minister may say these or other words of invitation:

The true bread of heaven gives life to the world.
Come, all who are hungry, come and eat.
Come, all who are thirsty, come and drink.

**26** Words such as the following are said during the distribution:

The body of Christ keep you in eternal life. **Amen.**

The blood of Christ keep you in eternal life. **Amen.**

**27** During the distribution there may be appropriate music.

**28** The elements that remain are covered with a white cloth.

THE SHARING OF THE BREAD AND WINE

**24** The presiding minister, those assisting with the distribution, and the people receive, according to local custom.

The presiding minister may say these or other words of invitation:

Christ is the true bread from heaven.
Whoever eats this bread will live for ever.

Draw near with faith.

**25** Words such as the following are said during the distribution:

The body of Christ given for you. **Amen.**

The blood of Christ shed for you. **Amen.**

**26** During the distribution there may be appropriate music.

**27** The elements that remain are covered with a white cloth.

## PRAYERS AND DISMISSAL

29 Silence

30 Let us pray.

**We thank you, Lord,
for feeding us with the bread of heaven
and the cup of salvation.
Keep us in your grace
and at the coming of Christ in glory
bring us with your saints
into the life of your kingdom. Amen.**

31 Hymn

32 The presiding minister says:

Christ the Sun of Righteousness
shine upon *you/us*
and prepare *your/our* hearts and souls
to meet him when he comes in glory;
and the blessing of God,
the Father, the Son and the Holy Spirit,
be *yours/ours*, now and always. **Amen.**

33 The presiding minister says:

The day of the Lord is surely coming.
Be faithful in worship,
unwavering in hope,
fervent in the work of God's kingdom
and all the more as you see the Day drawing
near.

**Amen. Come, Lord Jesus.**

## PRAYERS AND DISMISSAL

28 Silence

29 Let us pray.

**Father of all,
we give you thanks and praise,
that when we were still far off
you met us in your Son and brought us home.
Dying and living,
he declared your love, gave us grace, and
opened the gate of glory.
May we who share Christ's body live his
risen life;
we who drink his cup bring life to others;
we whom the Spirit lights give light to the
world.
Keep us firm in the hope that you have set
before us,
so we and all your children shall be free,
and the whole earth live to praise your
name;
through Jesus Christ our Lord. Amen.**

30 Hymn

31 The presiding minister says:

May he, who by his incarnation
gathered into one things earthly and
heavenly,
fill *your/our* lives with his light and joy and
peace;
and the blessing of God,
the Father, the Son and the Holy Spirit,
remain with *you/us* always. **Amen.**

32 The presiding minister says:

We go in the peace of Christ.

**Thanks be to God.**

# Lent and Passiontide, Easter Season

## We come together

## Lent and Passiontide

### THE GATHERING OF THE PEOPLE OF GOD

**1** The presiding minister says:

Grace and peace to you from God our Father and the Lord Jesus Christ.

2 Hymn

3 The commandments of the Lord Jesus may be read.

Our Lord Jesus Christ said: 'The first commandment is, "Hear, O Israel: the Lord our God, the Lord is one; you shall love the Lord your God with all your heart, and with all your soul, and with all your mind, and with all your strength." The second is this, "You shall love your neighbour as yourself." There is no other commandment greater than these.' 'I give you a new commandment, that you love one another. Just as I have loved you, you also should love one another.'

**Amen. Lord, have mercy.**

## Easter Season

### THE GATHERING OF THE PEOPLE OF GOD

**1** The presiding minister says:

Alleluia! Christ is risen!
**He is risen indeed! Alleluia!**

or, from the Sixth Sunday of Easter:

Alleluia! The Lord reigns!
**Let the earth rejoice! Alleluia!**

2 Hymn

3 Let us pray.

Glory to you, O God:
you raised Jesus from the grave,
bringing us victory over death
and giving us eternal life.

Glory to you, O Christ:
for us and for our salvation
you overcame death
and opened the gate to everlasting life.

Glory to you, O Holy Spirit:
you lead us into the truth
and breathe new life into us.

**4** The presiding minister says:

Let us pray.

**Lord, you are steadfast in your love
and infinite in your mercy;
you welcome sinners
and invite them to be your guests.
We confess our sins,
trusting in you to forgive us.**

Silence

We have yielded to temptation and sinned:

Lord, have mercy.
**Lord, have mercy.**

We have turned from our neighbours in their
    need:

Christ, have mercy.
**Christ, have mercy.**

We have resisted your word in our hearts:

Lord, have mercy.
**Lord, have mercy.**

Glory to you, Father, Son and Holy Spirit,
now and for ever.  **Amen.**

**4** The presiding minister says:

If we have fallen into despair,
**Lord, forgive us.**

If we have failed to hope in you,
**Lord, forgive us.**

If we have been fearful of death,
**Lord, forgive us.**

If we have forgotten the victory of Christ,
**Lord, forgive us.**

Silence

May the living God
raise *you/us* from despair,
give *you/us* victory over sin
and set *you/us* free in Christ.  **Amen.**

EITHER

The almighty and most merciful God
grant you pardon,
forgiveness of all your sins,
time for true repentance
and amendment of life,
and the grace and comfort of the Holy Spirit.
**Amen.**

OR

May almighty God
have mercy on us,
forgive us our sins,
and keep us in life eternal.  **Amen.**

**5** The collect of the day, or one of the following or some other prayer:

Until the Fifth Sunday in Lent:

> Almighty God,
> whose Son Jesus Christ
> fasted forty days in the wilderness
> and was tempted as we are, yet without sin:
> give us grace to discipline ourselves
> in obedience to your Spirit;
> and, as you know our weakness,
> so may we know your power to save;
> through Jesus Christ our Lord. **Amen.**

From the Fifth Sunday in Lent:

> Most merciful God,
> who by the death and resurrection
> of your Son Jesus Christ
> delivered and saved the world:
> grant that by faith in him
> who suffered on the cross,
> we may triumph in the power of his victory;
> through Jesus Christ our Lord. **Amen.**

**5** The collect

On Easter Day:

> Lord of all life and power,
> who through the mighty resurrection of your Son
> overcame the old order of sin and death
> to make all things new in him:
> grant that we, being dead to sin
> and alive to you in Jesus Christ,
> may reign with him in glory;
> to whom with you in the unity of the Holy Spirit
> be praise and honour, glory and might,
> now and in all eternity. **Amen.**

On other days of the Easter season before the Sixth Sunday of Easter, the collect of the day, or this or some other prayer:

> Almighty God,
> of your own free goodness and mercy
> you have created us,
> and through the resurrection
> of your only-begotten Son
> you have given us hope;
> guard us by your love
> and, in your wisdom, keep us in eternal life;
> through Jesus Christ our Lord. **Amen.**

From the Sixth Sunday of Easter to the Saturday before Pentecost, the collect of the day, or this or some other prayer:

> Almighty God,
> you have exalted your only Son, Jesus Christ,
> with great triumph to your kingdom in
>   heaven.
> Mercifully give us faith
> to know that, as he promised,
> he abides with us on earth to the end of time,
> who is alive and reigns
> with you and the Holy Spirit,
> one God now and for ever. **Amen.**

6 Hymn or *Saviour of the World*

Jesus, Saviour of the world,
come to us in your mercy:
**we look to you to save and help us.**

By your cross and your life laid down
you set your people free:
**we look to you to save and help us.**

When they were ready to perish
you saved your disciples:
**we look to you to come to our help.**

In the greatness of your mercy
loose us from our chains:
**forgive the sins of all your people.**

Make yourself known
as our saviour and mighty deliverer:
**save and help us that we may praise you.**

Come now and dwell with us, Lord Christ
 Jesus:
**hear our prayer and be with us always.**

And when you come in your glory:
**make us to be one with you
and to share the life of your kingdom.**

6 EITHER *Glory to God in the highest*

**Glory to God in the highest,
and peace to God's people on earth.**

**Lord God, heavenly King,
almighty God and Father,
we worship you, we give you thanks,
we praise you for your glory.**

**Lord Jesus Christ, only Son of the Father,
Lord God, Lamb of God,
you take away the sin of the world:
have mercy on us;
you are seated at the right hand of the Father:
receive our prayer.**

**For you alone are the Holy One,
you alone are the Lord,
you alone are the Most High, Jesus Christ,
with the Holy Spirit,
in the glory of God the Father.  Amen.**

OR (before the Sixth Sunday of Easter) *A Song of Resurrection*

Christ our Passover has been sacrificed for us,
so let us celebrate the feast,

not with the old leaven
of corruption and wickedness,
but with the unleavened bread
of sincerity and truth.

Christ once raised from the dead dies no more;
death has no more dominion over him.

**In dying, he died to sin once for all;
In living, he lives to God.**

See yourselves therefore as dead to sin
and alive to God in Jesus Christ our Lord.

**Christ has been raised from the dead;
the first fruits of those who sleep.**

For as by one man came death,
by another has come also the resurrection of
 the dead.

**For as in Adam all die,
even so in Christ shall all be made alive.**

Glory to the Father, and to the Son,
and to the Holy Spirit:
**as it was in the beginning, is now,
and shall be for ever.  Amen.**

## THE MINISTRY OF THE WORD

**Either two or three readings from scripture follow, the last of which is the Gospel.**

7  Old Testament reading

8  A Psalm or portion of a Psalm may be said or sung.

9  Epistle

10  Hymn

11  A reading from the Gospel according to . . .

Hear the Gospel of Christ.
**Glory to Christ our Saviour.**

The Gospel is read.

This is the Gospel of Christ.
**Praise to Christ our Lord.**

12  Sermon

---

OR (from the Sixth Sunday of Easter) *A Song of Christ's Glory*

**Christ Jesus was in the form of God,
but he did not cling to equality with God.
He emptied himself,
taking the form of a servant,
and was born in our human likeness.
Being found in human form,
he humbled himself
and became obedient unto death,
even death on a cross.
Therefore, God has highly exalted him,
and bestowed on him the name above every
name,
that at the name of Jesus every knee shall
bow,
in heaven and on earth and under the earth,
and every tongue confess that Jesus Christ
is Lord,
to the glory of God the Father.**

OR a hymn

## THE MINISTRY OF THE WORD

**Either two or three readings from scripture follow, the last of which is the Gospel.**

7  Reading from Acts or Old Testament reading

8  A Psalm or portion of a Psalm may be said or sung.

9  Epistle

10  Hymn

11  A reading from the Gospel according to . . .

Alleluia!  Hear the Gospel of Christ.
**Glory to Christ our Saviour.  Alleluia!**

The Gospel is read.

Alleluia!  This is the Gospel of Christ.
**Praise to Christ our Lord.  Alleluia!**

12  Sermon

13  Hymn

13 Affirmation of Faith: The Apostles' Creed

All stand.

**I believe in God, the Father almighty,
creator of heaven and earth.**

**I believe in Jesus Christ,
God's only Son, our Lord,
who was conceived by the Holy Spirit,
born of the Virgin Mary,
suffered under Pontius Pilate,
was crucified, died, and was buried;
he descended to the dead.
On the third day he rose again;
he ascended into heaven,
he is seated at the right hand of the Father,
and he will come to judge the living and the
    dead.**

**I believe in the Holy Spirit,
the holy catholic Church,
the communion of saints,
the forgiveness of sins,
the resurrection of the body,
and the life everlasting.  Amen.**

14 Hymn

**15** These or some other prayers of intercession:

Let us pray for the Church of God throughout
the world, for . . . and for . . .

Lord, hear us.
**Lord, graciously hear us.**

Let us pray for those who have power and
influence and for all who govern the nations,
for . . . and for . . .

Lord, hear us.
**Lord, graciously hear us.**

Let us pray for the powerless, for
all victims of famine and war,
and for all who strive for justice
and peace, for . . . and for . . .

Lord, hear us.
**Lord, graciously hear us.**

**14** These or some other prayers of intercession:

In the power of the resurrection we offer our
prayers to God.

Let us pray.

Remember, O Lord, in your love
    the Church throughout the world . . .
      those recently baptized and confirmed . . .
      those who minister to others . . .

Silence

May your whole Church know your power
and be a sign that Christ is risen.

Lord of life,
**hear us in your love.**

Let us pray for the afflicted and sorrowful and for all who need our prayers, for . . . and for . . .

Lord, hear us.
**Lord, graciously hear us.**

Let us remember before God those who have passed from this life in faith and obedience, giving thanks for . . . and for . . .

Lord, hear us.
**Lord, graciously hear us.**

Eternal God,
through the self-offering of your Son
you have filled our lives with your presence.
Help us in our sufferings and trials
and strengthen us in our weakness;
through Jesus Christ our Lord. **Amen.**

Remember in your love the world you have made . . .
   those who seek a fair and proper use of the world's resources . . .
   those who strive for justice and peace among the nations . . .

Silence

May the whole earth be transformed by mercy and rejoice in hope.

Lord of life,
**hear us in your love.**

Remember in your love those who suffer . . .
   the victims of violence and injustice . . .
   those who mourn . . .

Silence

May all in need find comfort, strength and freedom in the living Christ.

Lord of life,
**hear us in your love.**

Remember in your love those who have died:
   those who have confessed the faith
   and those whose faith is known to you alone.

Silence

May all your children receive grace and light according to their needs and come at last to share with all the saints in life eternal.

Lord of life,
**hear us in your love.**

Gracious God, we ask
these prayers through
Jesus Christ, our risen Lord
and Saviour.
**Amen.**

**15**  The Lord's Prayer

EITHER                                                    OR

We say together the prayer that Jesus gave us:          As our Saviour taught his disciples, we pray:

**Our Father in heaven,**                               **Our Father, who art in heaven,**
**hallowed be your Name,**                              **hallowed be thy Name;**
**your kingdom come,**                                  **thy kingdom come;**
**your will be done,**                                  **thy will be done;**
**on earth as in heaven.**                              **on earth as it is in heaven.**
**Give us today our daily bread.**                      **Give us this day our daily bread.**
**Forgive us our sins**                                 **And forgive us our trespasses,**
**as we forgive those who sin against us.**             **as we forgive those who trespass against us.**
**Save us from the time of trial**                      **And lead us not into temptation;**
**and deliver us from evil.**                           **but deliver us from evil.**
**For the kingdom, the power and**                      **For thine is the kingdom, the power,**
**  the glory are yours,**                              **  and the glory,**
**now and for ever.  Amen.**                            **for ever and ever.  Amen.**

16 The Nicene Creed

All stand.

Let us profess the faith of the Church.

**We believe in one God,
the Father, the Almighty,
maker of heaven and earth,
of all that is, seen and unseen.**

**We believe in one Lord, Jesus Christ,
the only Son of God,
eternally begotten of the Father,
God from God, Light from Light,
true God from true God,
begotten, not made,
of one Being with the Father;
through him all things were made.
For us and for our salvation
he came down from heaven,
was incarnate of the Holy Spirit and the
  Virgin Mary
and became truly human.
For our sake he was crucified under
  Pontius Pilate;
he suffered death and was buried.**

**On the third day he rose again
in accordance with the Scriptures;
he ascended into heaven
and is seated at the right hand of the Father.
He will come again in glory to judge the
  living and the dead,
and his kingdom will have no end.**

**We believe in the Holy Spirit, the Lord, the
  giver of life,
who proceeds from the Father and the Son,
who with the Father and the Son is
  worshipped and glorified,
who has spoken through the prophets.
We believe in one holy catholic and
  apostolic Church.
We acknowledge one Baptism for the
  forgiveness of sins.
We look for the resurrection of the dead,
and the life of the world to come. Amen.**

### THE LORD'S SUPPER

**16** The Peace

All stand.

In Christ, God was pleased to reconcile to himself all things, whether on earth or in heaven, by making peace through his blood which was shed on the cross.

The peace of the Lord be always with you.
**And also with you.**

### THE PREPARATION OF THE GIFTS

**17** Hymn

**18** The offerings of the people are presented. Bread and wine are brought to the table (or if already on the table are uncovered). The presiding minister takes the bread and wine and prepares them for use.

### THE LORD'S SUPPER

**17** The Peace

All stand.

The risen Christ came and stood among his disciples and said: 'Peace be with you!'

Then they were glad when they saw the Lord.

Alleluia! The peace of the risen Christ be always with you.
**And also with you. Alleluia!**

The people may greet one another in the name of the risen Lord.

### THE PREPARATION OF THE GIFTS

**18** Hymn

**19** The offerings of the people are presented. Bread and wine are brought to the table (or if already on the table are uncovered).

The presiding minister takes the bread and lifts it in the sight of the people, saying:

Here is bread, God's good gift.
**It will become for us the bread of life.**

The presiding minister takes the cup and lifts it in the sight of the people, saying:

Here is wine, God's good gift.
**It will become for us the cup of salvation.**

THE THANKSGIVING

**19** All stand.

The presiding minister leads the great prayer of thanksgiving:

The Lord be with you.
**And also with you.**

Lift up your hearts.
**We lift them to the Lord.**

Let us give thanks to the Lord our God.
**It is right to give our thanks and praise.**

Blessing and praise belong to you,
gracious and eternal God.

Through your living Word
you created all things,
the majesty of the heavens
and the glory of the earth.
In your wisdom and goodness

you have made all people
in your image and likeness.

Therefore with saints and angels
and with all creation
we lift up our voices
to proclaim the glory of your name:

**Holy, holy, holy Lord,**
**God of power and might,**
**heaven and earth are full of your glory.**
**Hosanna in the highest.**
**Blessèd is he who comes in the name of the**
    **Lord.**
**Hosanna in the highest.**

Holy and gracious God,
we give you thanks and praise
that in the fullness of time
you gave your only Son
to share our human nature
and to be tempted in every way as we are,
yet without sin;
to set his face resolutely towards Jerusalem
and to be lifted high upon the cross,
that he might draw all creation to himself.

THE THANKSGIVING

**20** All stand.

The presiding minister leads the great prayer of thanksgiving:

The Lord be with you.
**And also with you.**

Lift up your hearts.
**We lift them to the Lord.**

Let us give thanks to the Lord our God.
**It is right to give our thanks and praise.**

Blessing and honour, glory and power,
are rightly yours, all-gracious God.
By your creative word
you brought the world to birth;
in your generous love
you made the human family,
that we might see your glory
and live for ever in your presence.

**Blessing and honour, glory and power,**
**are rightly yours, all-gracious God.**

When we wandered from you in our sin
you sought us with your steadfast love
and did not give us up.
In the fullness of time you sent your Son
to be our Saviour and Deliverer.
Made of flesh and blood, he lived our life
and died our death upon the cross.
Death could not hold him
and now he reigns at your right hand.

**Blessing and honour, glory and power,**
**are rightly yours, all-gracious God.**

Therefore with angels and archangels
and all the company of heaven
we bless and praise your glorious name,
    saying:

**Holy, holy, holy Lord,**
**God of power and might,**
**heaven and earth are full of your glory.**
**Hosanna in the highest.**
**Blessèd is he who comes in the name of the**
    **Lord.**
**Hosanna in the highest.**

When the hour of his glory came,
and loving his own to the end,
he sat with them at supper,
took bread and, after giving thanks to you,
he broke it and gave it to his disciples, saying,
'Take, eat.  This is my body which is for you.
Do this in remembrance of me.'

In the same way
he took the cup after supper, saying,
'Drink from this, all of you;
this cup is the new covenant in my blood.
Do this, whenever you drink it,
in remembrance of me.'

**Dying, you destroyed our death.
Rising, you restored our life.
Lord Jesus, come in glory.**

In obedience to his command
we recall his suffering and death,
his resurrection and ascension,
and we look for his coming in glory.

Send your Holy Spirit
that these gifts of bread and wine
may be for us the body and blood of Christ.

In union with Christ's offering for us,
we offer ourselves as a holy and living
    sacrifice.
Unite us in love and peace with all your
    people
until, with the whole company of heaven,
we are brought into the presence of your
    eternal glory,
through Jesus Christ our Lord.

**Through him, with him, and in him,
in the unity of the Holy Spirit,
all honour and glory are yours,
almighty Father, now and for ever.  Amen.**

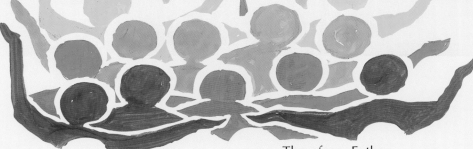

Blessèd indeed is the Lord Jesus Christ
who, at supper with his friends,
took bread and gave you thanks,
broke it, gave it to them and said:
'Take this, all of you, and eat it.
This is my body given for you.
Do this in remembrance of me.'

When supper was ended,
he took the cup and gave you thanks,
gave it to them, and said:
'Drink from it all of you.
This is my blood of the new covenant,
poured out for you and for everyone,
for the forgiveness of sins.
Do this in remembrance of me.'

**Dying, you destroyed our death.
Rising, you restored our life.
Lord Jesus, come in glory.**

Therefore, Father,
we celebrate this Passover of gladness;
for as in Adam all die,
even so in Christ shall all be made alive.
Accept, through him, our great high priest,
this, our sacrifice of praise.

Send your Holy Spirit
that these gifts of bread and wine
may be for us the body and the blood of
    Christ.
Gather us, who share this feast,
into the kingdom of your glory
that with all your people in every time and
    place
we may praise and worship you for ever;
through Jesus Christ our Lord,

**by whom and with whom
in the unity of the Holy Spirit,
all honour and glory are yours,
heavenly Father, now and always.  Amen.**

**20** The Lord's Prayer

EITHER

We say together the prayer that Jesus gave us:

**Our Father in heaven,
hallowed be your Name,
your kingdom come,
your will be done,
on earth as in heaven.
Give us today our daily bread.
Forgive us our sins
as we forgive those who sin against us.
Save us from the time of trial
and deliver us from evil.
For the kingdom, the power and
the glory are yours,
now and for ever.  Amen.**

OR

As our Saviour taught his disciples, we pray:

**Our Father, who art in heaven,
hallowed be thy Name;
thy kingdom come;
thy will be done;
on earth as it is in heaven.
Give us this day our daily bread.
And forgive us our trespasses,
as we forgive those who trespass against us.
And lead us not into temptation;
but deliver us from evil.
For thine is the kingdom, the power,
and the glory,
for ever and ever.  Amen.**

# THEY RECOGNISED HIM

THE BREAKING OF THE BREAD

**21** The presiding minister breaks the bread in the sight of the people in silence, or saying:

The bread we break is a sharing in the body of Christ.
**Christ is the Bread of Life.**

The presiding minister may lift the cup in silence, or saying:

The cup we take is a sharing in the blood of Christ.
**Christ is the True Vine.**

**22** Silence, all seated or kneeling

**23** **Jesus, Lamb of God, have mercy on us.**
**Jesus, bearer of our sins, have mercy on us.**
**Jesus, redeemer of the world, grant us peace.**

**24** EITHER

Let us pray.

**We do not presume**
**to come to this your table, merciful Lord,**
**trusting in our own righteousness,**
**but in your manifold and great mercies.**

**We are not worthy**
**so much as to gather up the crumbs under**
**your table.**
**But you are the same Lord**
**whose nature is always to have mercy.**
**Grant us therefore, gracious Lord,**
**so to eat the flesh of your dear Son**
**Jesus Christ,**
**and to drink his blood,**
**that we may evermore dwell in him**
**and he in us. Amen.**

OR

We say together:

**Lord, we come to your table,**
**trusting in your mercy**
**and not in any goodness of our own.**
**We are not worthy**
**even to gather up the crumbs under your**
**table,**
**but it is your nature always to have mercy,**
**and on that we depend.**
**So feed us with the body and blood**
**of Jesus Christ, your Son,**
**that we may for ever live in him**
**and he in us. Amen.**

THE BREAKING OF THE BREAD

**21** The presiding minister breaks the bread in the sight of the people in silence, or saying:

Alleluia! Christ our Passover is sacrificed for us.
**Therefore let us keep the feast. Alleluia!**

OR, after the Sixth Sunday of Easter:

The things of God for God's holy people.

**Jesus Christ is holy;**
**Jesus Christ is Lord.**
**Glory to God the Father.**

**22** Silence, all seated or kneeling

# AT THE
# BREAKING OF THE BREAD

### THE SHARING OF THE BREAD AND WINE

**25** The presiding minister, those assisting with the distribution, and the people receive, according to local custom.

The presiding minister may say these or other words of invitation:

EITHER

> Receive this holy sacrament
> of the body and blood of Christ
> and feed on the Lamb of God
> with reverence and with faith.

OR

> Come to this sacred table,
> not because you must but because you may;
> come, not to declare that you are righteous,
> but that you desire to be true disciples of our
>    Lord Jesus Christ:
> come, not because you are strong,
> but because you are weak;
> not because you have any claim on heaven's
>    rewards,
> but because in your frailty and sin
> you stand in constant need of heaven's mercy
>    and help.

**26** Words such as the following are said during the distribution:

> The body of Christ given for you. **Amen.**

> The blood of Christ shed for you. **Amen.**

**27** The elements that remain are covered with a white cloth.

### THE SHARING OF THE BREAD AND WINE

**23** The presiding minister, those assisting with the distribution, and the people receive, according to local custom.

The presiding minister may say these or other words of invitation:

> We meet the risen Christ in the breaking of
>    the bread.

> Draw near with faith.

**24** Words such as the following are said during the distribution:

> The body of Christ keep you in eternal life.
> **Amen.**

> The blood of Christ keep you in eternal life.
> **Amen.**

25 During the distribution there may be appropriate music.

**26** The elements that remain are covered with a white cloth.

PRAYERS AND DISMISSAL

**28** Silence

**29** Let us pray.

**Gracious God,**
**we thank you that you have nourished us**
**with the bread of life**
**and with the cup of salvation.**
**May we who have received this sacrament**
**be strengthened in your service;**
**we who have sung your praises**
**live in your glory;**
**and we who have known**
**the greatness of your love**
**see you face to face in your kingdom;**
**through Jesus Christ our Lord.  Amen.**

PRAYERS AND DISMISSAL

**27** Silence

**28** Let us pray.

EITHER

**A**  **God of our salvation,**
**we thank you for our communion**
**with the risen Christ**
**and with all who love him in**
**earth and heaven.**
**We pray that, strengthened by his grace,**
**we may serve you faithfully all our days;**
**through Jesus Christ our Lord.  Amen.**

OR

**B**  **Lord our God, we give you thanks**
**because you have delivered us from the**
**power of darkness**
**and brought us into the kingdom of your**
**Son.**
**Grant that, as by his resurrection**
**we are brought to new life,**
**so by his continued reign in us**
**we may be brought to eternal joy;**
**through the same Christ our Lord.  Amen.**

30 Hymn

31 The presiding minister says:

> The God of all grace
> who has called *you/us* to eternal glory in
>   Christ,
> make *you/us* perfect,
> confirming and strengthening *you/us;*
> and to him be the power for ever and ever.
> **Amen.**

> The almighty and merciful Lord,
> the Father, the Son and the Holy Spirit,
> bless *you/us* and keep *you/us,*
> now and always.  **Amen.**

**32** The presiding minister says:

> Go in peace to love and serve the Lord.
>
> **In the name of Christ.  Amen.**

29 Hymn

30 The presiding minister says:

EITHER  (before the Sixth Sunday of Easter)

A  God the Father,
   by whose glory Christ was raised from the
     dead,
   strengthen *you/us*
   to walk with him in his risen life;
   and may almighty God bless *you/us,*
   the Father, the Son and the Holy Spirit.  **Amen.**

   OR (from the Sixth Sunday of Easter)

B  Christ our King
   make *you/us* faithful and strong to do his will
   that *you/we* may reign with him in glory;
   and may almighty God bless *you/us,*
   the Father, the Son and the Holy Spirit.  **Amen.**

**31** The presiding minister says:

> Alleluia!
> Go in joy and peace to love and serve the Lord.
>
> **In the name of Christ.  Alleluia!**

# Pentecost
## and Times of Renewal

### We come together
### We say we are sorry

## Pentecost

THE GATHERING OF THE PEOPLE OF GOD

**1** The presiding minister says:

> God declares:
> I will pour out my Spirit on all flesh.
> Then everyone who calls on the name of the
> Lord shall be saved.

**2** Hymn

**3** Let us pray.

> **Come, Holy Spirit,**
> **fill the hearts of your faithful people,**
> **and kindle in us the fire of your love;**
> **through Jesus Christ our Lord.  Amen.**

**4** The presiding minister says:

> Let us confess our sins to God.

Silence

> **Gracious and holy God,**
> **we confess that we have sinned**
> **against you and against our neighbour.**
> **Your Spirit gives light,**
> **  but we have preferred darkness;**
> **your Spirit gives wisdom,**
> **  but we have been foolish;**
> **your Spirit gives power,**
> **  but we have trusted in our own strength.**
> **For the sake of Jesus Christ, your Son,**
> **forgive our sins,**
> **and enable us by your Spirit**
> **to serve you in joyful obedience,**
> **to the glory of your Name.  Amen.**

> There is now no condemnation
> for those who live in union with Christ Jesus;
> for the law of the Spirit of life
> has set us free from the law of sin and death.

> **Amen.  Thanks be to God.**

**5** The collect of the day, or this or some other prayer:

> Faithful God,
> you fulfilled the promise of Easter
> by sending your Holy Spirit
> and opening the way of eternal life
> to all the human race.
> Keep us in the unity of your Spirit,
> that every tongue may tell of your glory;
> through Jesus Christ our Lord,
> who is alive and reigns with you,
> in the unity of the Holy Spirit,
> one God, now and for ever.  **Amen.**

**6** Hymn or *Glory to God in the highest*

> **Glory to God in the highest,**
> **and peace to God's people on earth.**
>
> **Lord God, heavenly King,**
> **almighty God and Father,**
> **we worship you, we give you thanks,**
> **we praise you for your glory.**
>
> **Lord Jesus Christ, only Son of the Father,**
> **Lord God, Lamb of God,**
> **you take away the sin of the world:**
> **have mercy on us;**
> **you are seated at the right hand of the**
> **Father:**
> **receive our prayer.**
>
> **For you alone are the Holy One,**
> **you alone are the Lord,**
> **you alone are the Most High, Jesus Christ,**
> **with the Holy Spirit,**
> **in the glory of God the Father.  Amen.**

## THE MINISTRY OF THE WORD

**Either two or three readings from scripture follow, the last of which is the Gospel.**

**7** Old Testament reading or, on the Day of Pentecost, a reading from Acts.

**8** A Psalm or portion of a Psalm may be said or sung.

**9** Epistle

**10** Hymn

**11**   A reading from the Gospel according to . . .

> Hear the Gospel of Christ.
> **Glory to Christ our Saviour.**

The Gospel is read.

> This is the Gospel of Christ.
> **Praise to Christ our Lord.**

**12** Sermon

**13** There may be a time of quiet reflection or testimony.

**14** These or some other prayers of intercession:

Gracious God,
whose Spirit helps us in our weakness
and guides us in our prayers,
we pray for the Church and for the world
in the name of Jesus Christ.

Renew the life and faith of the Church;
strengthen our witness;
and make us one in Christ . . .
Grant that we and all who confess that
   Christ is Lord
may be faithful in your service
and filled with the Spirit,
that the world may be turned to you.

Lord, in your mercy,
**hear our prayer.**

Guide the nations
in the ways of justice, liberty and peace;
and help them to seek
the unity and welfare of all people . . .
Give to all in authority
wisdom to know and strength to do
   what is right.

Lord, in your mercy,
**hear our prayer.**

Comfort those in sorrow;
heal the sick in body or in mind
and deliver the oppressed . . .
Grant us compassion for all who suffer,
and help us so to carry one another's burdens
that we may fulfil the law of Christ.

Lord, in your mercy,
**hear our prayer.**

Receive our thanks and praise
for all who have served you faithfully here
   on earth,
and especially those who have revealed to us
your grace in Christ . . .
May we and all your people
share the life and joy of your kingdom;
through Jesus Christ our Lord.  **Amen.**

15 The Peace

All stand.

We are the Body of Christ.

**In the one Spirit
we were all baptized into one body.
Let us therefore keep the unity of the Spirit
in the bond of peace.**

The peace of the Lord be always with you.
**And also with you.**

The people may greet one another in the name
of Christ.

16  The Nicene Creed

All stand.

Let us profess the faith of the Church.

**We believe in one God,**
**the Father, the Almighty,**
**maker of heaven and earth,**
**of all that is, seen and unseen.**

**We believe in one Lord, Jesus Christ,**
**the only Son of God,**
**eternally begotten of the Father,**
**God from God, Light from Light,**
**true God from true God,**
**begotten, not made,**
**of one Being with the Father;**
**through him all things were made.**
**For us and for our salvation**
**he came down from heaven,**
**was incarnate of the Holy Spirit and the**
**  Virgin Mary**
**and became truly human.**
**For our sake he was crucified under**
**  Pontius Pilate;**
**he suffered death and was buried.**
**On the third day he rose again**
**in accordance with the Scriptures;**
**he ascended into heaven**
**and is seated at the right hand of the Father.**
**He will come again in glory to judge the**
**  living and the dead,**
**and his kingdom will have no end.**

**We believe in the Holy Spirit, the Lord, the**
**  giver of life,**
**who proceeds from the Father and the Son,**
**who with the Father and the Son is**
**  worshipped and glorified,**
**who has spoken through the prophets.**
**We believe in one holy catholic and**
**  apostolic Church.**
**We acknowledge one Baptism for the**
**  forgiveness of sins.**
**We look for the resurrection of the dead,**
**and the life of the world to come.  Amen.**

THE LORD'S SUPPER

THE PREPARATION OF THE GIFTS

17  Hymn

**18**  The offerings of the people are presented.
Bread and wine are brought to the table (or if
already on the table are uncovered).  The
presiding minister takes the bread and wine
and prepares them for use.

# We give thanks

**19** All stand.

The presiding minister leads the great prayer of thanksgiving:

The Lord be with you.
**And also with you.**

Lift up your hearts.
**We lift them to the Lord.**

Let us give thanks to the Lord our God.
**It is right to give our thanks and praise.**

It is indeed right,
it is our duty and our joy,
gracious and holy Father,
always and everywhere to give you thanks.

In the beginning
your Spirit swept across the face of the
    waters,
bringing order and beauty out of chaos.
You formed us in your image
and breathed into us the breath of life.
Though we turned away from you,
your love remained steadfast,
and you sent your only Son Jesus Christ
to be the Saviour of the world.

At his Baptism in the Jordan
he was anointed by your Spirit
and revealed as your beloved Son.
In the power of the Spirit
he was sent to preach good news to the poor,
to proclaim release to the captives
and recovery of sight to the blind,
to set at liberty those who are oppressed,
and to announce that the time had come
when you would save your people.

Sharing our human nature,
he died on the cross.
Raised again in glory,
he lives for ever to pray for us.
By the gift of the Spirit,
whom you have sent in his name,
you bring to completion the work of your
    Son,
leading us into all truth,
making us a people for your praise
and giving us power to proclaim the Gospel
in all the world.

And so, with all the faithful of every time
    and place,
we join with choirs of angels in the eternal
    hymn:

**Holy, holy, holy Lord,**
**God of power and might,**
**heaven and earth are full of your glory.**
**Hosanna in the highest.**
**Blessèd is he who comes in the name of the**
    **Lord.**
**Hosanna in the highest.**

On the night before he died,
the Lord Jesus took bread and gave you thanks.
He broke it, and gave it to his disciples,
    saying,
'Take, eat. This is my body, given for you.
Do this in remembrance of me.'

After supper, he took the cup of wine.
He gave thanks, and gave it to them, saying,
'Drink from it, all of you.
This is my blood of the new covenant,
poured out for all people
for the forgiveness of sins.
Do this in remembrance of me.'

And so,
in remembrance of all his mighty acts,
we offer you these gifts,
and with them ourselves
as a holy, living sacrifice.

**You send forth your Spirit.**
**You bind us in love.**
**You renew the face of the earth.**

Pour out your Holy Spirit
that these gifts of bread and wine
may be for us the body and blood of Christ.
Unite us with him and with one another
in mission to all the world;
and bring us with the whole creation
to your heavenly kingdom.

**Through Christ, with Christ, in Christ,**
**in the unity of the Holy Spirit,**
**all blessing and honour and glory and power**
**be yours for ever and ever. Amen.**

**20** The Lord's Prayer

EITHER

We say together the prayer that Jesus gave us:

**Our Father in heaven,
hallowed be your Name,
your kingdom come,
your will be done,
on earth as in heaven.
Give us today our daily bread.
Forgive us our sins
as we forgive those who sin against us.
Save us from the time of trial
and deliver us from evil.
For the kingdom, the power and
   the glory are yours,
now and for ever.  Amen.**

OR

As our Saviour taught his disciples, we pray:

**Our Father, who art in heaven,
hallowed be thy Name;
thy kingdom come;
thy will be done;
on earth as it is in heaven.
Give us this day our daily bread.
And forgive us our trespasses,
as we forgive those who trespass against us.
And lead us not into temptation;
but deliver us from evil.
For thine is the kingdom, the power,
   and the glory,
for ever and ever.  Amen.**

## The bread is broken

### THE BREAKING OF THE BREAD

**21** The presiding minister breaks the bread in the sight of the people in silence, or saying:

On the Day of Pentecost:

> Alleluia! Christ our Passover is sacrificed for us.
> **Therefore let us keep the feast. Alleluia!**

At other times:

> We break this bread to share in the body of Christ.
>
> **Though we are many, we are one body, because we all share in one bread.**

**22** Silence, all seated or kneeling

## We share the bread and wine

### THE SHARING OF THE BREAD AND WINE

**23** The presiding minister, those assisting with the distribution, and the people receive, according to local custom.

The presiding minister may say these or other words of invitation:

> Receive this holy sacrament
> of the body and blood of Christ,
> and feed on the Lamb of God
> with reverence and with faith.

**24** Words such as the following are said during the distribution:

> The body of Christ keep you in eternal life.
> **Amen.**

> The blood of Christ keep you in eternal life.
> **Amen.**

**25** During the distribution there may be appropriate music.

**26** The elements that remain are covered with a white cloth.

## PRAYERS AND DISMISSAL

27  Silence

28    Let us pray.

**God of power,**
**may the boldness of your Spirit transform us,**
**may the gentleness of your Spirit lead us,**
**and may the gifts of your Spirit equip us**
**to serve and worship you**
**now and always.  Amen.**

29  Hymn

30  The presiding minister says:

The Spirit of truth lead *you/us* into all truth,
give *you/us* grace to confess that Jesus Christ
    is Lord,
and to proclaim the word and works of God;
and the blessing of God,
Spirit, Son and Father,
remain with *you/us* always.  **Amen.**

**31**  The presiding minister says:

We go into the world in the power of the Spirit
to fulfil our high calling as servants of Christ.

**Thanks be to God.  Amen.**

# Ordinary Seasons
## First, Second and Third Services

## We come together

**First
Service**

THE GATHERING OF THE PEOPLE OF GOD

1  The presiding minister reads a sentence of scripture.

2  Hymn

3  Let us pray.

**Almighty God,
to whom all hearts are open,
all desires known,
and from whom no secrets are hidden:
cleanse the thoughts of our hearts
by the inspiration of your Holy Spirit,
that we may perfectly love you,
and worthily magnify your holy Name;
through Christ our Lord.  Amen.**

**Second
Service**

THE GATHERING OF THE PEOPLE OF GOD

1  The presiding minister says:

God's grace and peace are with us.
Let our hearts be filled with joy.

2  Hymn

**Third
Service**

THE GATHERING OF THE PEOPLE OF GOD

1  The presiding minister says:

The grace of the Lord Jesus Christ,
and the love of God,
and the fellowship of the Holy Spirit,
be with you all.  **Amen.**

2  Hymn

3  Let us pray.

**Give us, O God, a vision of your glory,
that we may worship you in spirit and in truth,
and offer the praise of glad and thankful
    hearts;
through Christ our Lord.  Amen.**

**4**   The presiding minister says:

Let us confess our sins to God.

**Most merciful God,
we confess that we have sinned against you
in thought and word and deed.
We have not loved you with our whole heart.
We have not loved our neighbours as
   ourselves.**

Silence

In your mercy,

**forgive what we have been,
help us to amend what we are,
and direct what we shall be;**

**that we may delight in your will
and walk in your ways;
through Jesus Christ our Lord.  Amen.**

If we confess our sins,
God is faithful and just
and will forgive our sins,
and cleanse us from all unrighteousness.
**Amen.  Thanks be to God.**

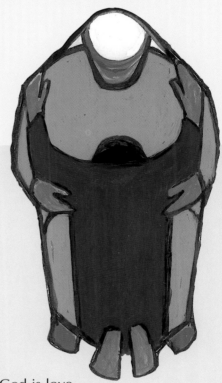

God is love
and forgives our sins through Jesus.  **Amen.**

**3**   The presiding minister says:

Let us pray.

**God of mercy,
your love for us is strong,
but our love for you is weak.
You call us to follow Jesus,
but we are slow to obey.
You care for all that you have made,
but we ignore the needs of others
and misuse your creation.
We are sorry for our sins.
Forgive us,
and help us to please you
by the way we live;
through Jesus Christ our Lord.  Amen.**

**4**   The presiding minister says:

Let us call to mind our sins.

Silence

Lord Jesus, you came into the world to save
   sinners:

Lord, have mercy.
**Lord, have mercy.**

We have brought sorrow and hurt to you,
to others and to ourselves:

Christ, have mercy.
**Christ, have mercy.**

You give yourself to heal and renew us,
and to bring us strength:

Lord, have mercy.
**Lord, have mercy.**

EITHER

May almighty God
have mercy on us,
forgive us our sins,
and keep us in life eternal.  **Amen.**

OR

Know that your sins are forgiven
through Jesus Christ, our Saviour,
and rejoice in his goodness and grace.
**Amen.  Thanks be to God.**

**5** The collect of the day, or this or some other prayer:

> Gracious God,
> whose love for the world is revealed in your
>   Son our Saviour:
> grant that he may live in our hearts by faith,
> and be proclaimed in our lives by love;
> through the same Jesus Christ our Lord,
> to whom with you and the Holy Spirit
> be glory and praise, now and for ever. **Amen.**

**6** ***Glory to God in the highest***, a hymn, or some other canticle of praise

> **Glory to God in the highest,**
> **and peace to God's people on earth.**
>
> **Lord God, heavenly King,**
> **almighty God and Father,**
> **we worship you, we give you thanks,**
> **we praise you for your glory.**

**4** The collect of the day, or this or some other prayer:

> Generous God,
> you gave your Son for the life of the
>   whole world.
> Give us the joy of knowing the risen Christ,
> and let your Holy Spirit guide us,
> that we may love and serve you on earth
> and live with you for ever in heaven;
> through Jesus Christ our Lord. **Amen.**

**5** Hymn or one of these versions of ***Glory to God*** or some other act of praise

A

**5** The collect of the day, or this or some other prayer:

> God, the source of all wisdom,
> you teach us in your word
> that love is the fulfilling of the law:
> grant that we may love you with all our heart
> and our neighbours as ourselves;
> through Jesus Christ our Lord. **Amen.**

**6** Hymn or ***You are Worthy*** or a short time of praise

> **You are worthy, our Lord and God;**
> **to receive glory and honour and power,**
> **for you have created all things:**
> **and by your will they were created and have**
> **  their being.**
> **You are worthy, O Christ,**
> **for you were slain:**

Lord Jesus Christ, only Son of the Father,
Lord God, Lamb of God,
you take away the sin of the world:
have mercy on us;
you are seated at the right hand of the
 Father:
receive our prayer.

For you alone are the Holy One,
you alone are the Lord,
you alone are the Most High, Jesus Christ,
with the Holy Spirit,
in the glory of God the Father.  Amen.

B  Glory to God in the highest,
and peace to God's people on earth.

Lord God, heavenly King,
almighty God and Father,
we worship you, we give you thanks,
we praise you for your glory.

Lord Jesus Christ, only Son of the Father,
Lord God, Lamb of God,
you take away the sin of the world:
have mercy on us;
you are seated at the right hand of the
 Father:
receive our prayer.

For you alone are the Holy One,
you alone are the Lord,
you alone are the Most High, Jesus Christ,
with the Holy Spirit,
in the glory of God the Father.  Amen.

and with your blood
you redeemed the human race for God,
and have chosen us to be a holy priesthood
from every people and nation.
To the One who is seated on the throne
and to the Lamb:
be blessing and honour, glory and might,
for ever and ever.  Amen.

## THE MINISTRY OF THE WORD

**Either two or three readings from scripture follow, the last of which is the Gospel.**

7 Old Testament reading

8 A Psalm or portion of a Psalm may be said or sung.

9 Epistle

10 Hymn

11 A reading from the Gospel according to . . .

Hear the Gospel of Christ.
**Glory to Christ our Saviour.**

The Gospel is read.

This is the Gospel of Christ.
**Praise to Christ our Lord.**

**12** Sermon

13 Hymn

## THE MINISTRY OF THE WORD

**Either two or three readings from scripture follow, the last of which is the Gospel.**

6 Old Testament reading

7 A Psalm or portion of a Psalm may be said or sung.

8 Epistle

9 Hymn or Alleluia

Al - le - lu - ia, Al - le - lu - ia, Al - le - lu - ia!

**10** A reading from the Gospel according to . . .

Hear the Gospel of Christ.
**Glory to Christ our Saviour.**

The Gospel is read.

This is the Gospel of Christ.
**Praise to Christ our Lord.**

**11** Sermon

## THE MINISTRY OF THE WORD

**Either two or three readings from scripture follow, the last of which is the Gospel.**

7 Old Testament reading

8 A Psalm or portion of a Psalm may be said or sung.

9 Epistle

10 Hymn

**11** A reading from the Gospel according to . . .

Hear the Gospel of Christ.
**Glory to Christ our Saviour.**

The Gospel is read.

This is the Gospel of Christ.
**Praise to Christ our Lord.**

**12** Sermon

13 There may be a time of quiet reflection or testimony.

14 Hymn

12 EITHER

**A**  The Nicene Creed

All stand.

Let us profess the faith of the Church.

**We believe in one God,
the Father, the Almighty,
maker of heaven and earth,
of all that is, seen and unseen.**

**We believe in one Lord, Jesus Christ,
the only Son of God,
eternally begotten of the Father,
God from God, Light from Light,**

**true God from true God,
begotten, not made,
of one Being with the Father;
through him all things were made.
For us and for our salvation
he came down from heaven,
was incarnate of the Holy Spirit and the
    Virgin Mary
and became truly human.
For our sake he was crucified under
    Pontius Pilate;
he suffered death and was buried.
On the third day he rose again
in accordance with the Scriptures;
he ascended into heaven
and is seated at the right hand of the Father.**

WE BELIEVE

He will come again in glory to judge the
   living and the dead,
and his kingdom will have no end.

We believe in the Holy Spirit, the Lord, the
   giver of life,
who proceeds from the Father and the Son,
who with the Father and the Son is
   worshipped and glorified,
who has spoken through the prophets.
We believe in one holy catholic and
   apostolic Church.
We acknowledge one Baptism for the
   forgiveness of sins.
We look for the resurrection of the dead,
and the life of the world to come.  Amen.

OR

B An Affirmation of Faith

All stand.

Do you believe and trust in God the Father who
has created the universe?
**We believe and trust in God the Father.**

Do you believe and trust in Jesus, the Son of
God, who has redeemed the world?
**We believe and trust in God the Son.**

Do you believe and trust in the Holy Spirit,
who gives life to the people of God?
**We believe and trust in God the Holy Spirit.**

**14** These or some other prayers of intercession:

Let us pray.

God, most gracious and most holy,
grant us the help of your Spirit
as we pray for the Church and the world.

We pray for the Church in every land . . .
for this church and for other local churches . . .
that we may worship and serve you
with reverence and joy.

Silence

Lord, hear us.
**Lord, graciously hear us.**

We pray for the peoples of the world . . .
and for the leaders of the nations . . .
that all may work together for justice and peace.

Silence

Lord, hear us.
**Lord, graciously hear us.**

We pray for those who are ill or distressed . . .
for the lonely and the bereaved . . .
and for those in any other need or trouble . . .
that they may be comforted and sustained.

**13** Prayers of intercession

for the universal Church,
for peace and justice in the world,
for those in authority,
for the concerns of the local community,
for those who suffer;
thanksgiving for the departed.

A sung or spoken versicle and response may
conclude each section.

**15** These or some other prayers of intercession:

In faith let us pray to God our Father,
in the name of his Son, Jesus Christ,
and in the power of the Holy Spirit.

God of love, we pray for the life of your Church throughout the world . . . May every congregation be a community of love and every Christian a witness to your grace. Renew all who worship in this place that we may be a living fellowship in your Spirit and serve our neighbourhood.

Your kingdom come.
**Your will be done.**

God of mercy, we pray for the life of the world . . . and for those who exercise power . . . Show us how to live as members of the human family; to reject the ways of war; to bear each other's burdens and to work together for justice and peace.

Your kingdom come.
**Your will be done.**

God of compassion, we pray for those who are ill or anxious at home or in hospital . . . We pray for those whose lives are filled with fear and despair . . . Draw near with your saving love and bring healing and hope.

Your kingdom come.
**Your will be done.**

Silence

Lord, hear us.
**Lord, graciously hear us.**

Father, we remember before you
all your servants who have died in the faith
  of Christ . . .

We pray that we too may lead faithful and
  godly lives in this world,
and finally share with all the saints in
  everlasting joy;
through Jesus Christ our Lord.  **Amen.**

**15** The Lord's Prayer
EITHER

We say together the prayer that Jesus gave us:

**Our Father in heaven,
hallowed be your Name,
your kingdom come,
your will be done,
on earth as in heaven.
Give us today our daily bread.
Forgive us our sins
as we forgive those who sin against us.
Save us from the time of trial
and deliver us from evil.
For the kingdom, the power and
  the glory are yours,
now and for ever.  Amen.**

God of glory, we rejoice in the communion of
saints; we remember all who have faithfully
lived and all who have died in Christian
hope, especially . . .  Help us to follow their
example and bring us with them into the
fullness of your eternal joy.

Your kingdom come.
**Your will be done.**

Merciful God,
you have prepared for those who love you
such good things as pass our understanding;
pour into our hearts such love towards you
that we, loving you above all things,
may obtain your promises,
which exceed all that we can desire;
through Jesus Christ our Lord.  **Amen.**

OR

As our Saviour taught his disciples, we pray:

**Our Father, who art in heaven,
hallowed be thy Name;
thy kingdom come;
thy will be done;
on earth as it is in heaven.
Give us this day our daily bread.
And forgive us our trespasses,
as we forgive those who trespass against us.
And lead us not into temptation;
but deliver us from evil.
For thine is the kingdom, the power,
  and the glory,
for ever and ever.  Amen.**

16 The Peace

All stand.

We are the Body of Christ.

**In the one Spirit
we were all baptized into one body.
Let us therefore keep the unity of the Spirit
in the bond of peace.**

The peace of the Lord be always with you.
**And also with you.**

The people may greet one another in the name
of Christ.

THE LORD'S SUPPER

14 The Peace

All stand.

Our Lord Jesus Christ said:
'I leave you peace, my peace I give to you.'

The peace of the Lord be always with you.
**And also with you.**

The people may greet one another in the name
of Christ.

THE LORD'S SUPPER

16 The Peace

All stand.

Our Lord Jesus Christ said to the apostles:
'I leave you peace, my peace I give to you.'

The peace of the Lord be always with you.
**And also with you.**

The people may greet one another in the name
of Christ.

17 The Nicene Creed

All stand.

Let us profess the faith of the Church.

**We believe in one God,
the Father, the Almighty,
maker of heaven and earth,
of all that is, seen and unseen.**

**We believe in one Lord, Jesus Christ,
the only Son of God,
eternally begotten of the Father,
God from God, Light from Light,
true God from true God,
begotten, not made,
of one Being with the Father;**

**through him all things were made.
For us and for our salvation
he came down from heaven,
was incarnate of the Holy Spirit and the
  Virgin Mary
and became truly human.
For our sake he was crucified under
  Pontius Pilate;
he suffered death and was buried.
On the third day he rose again
in accordance with the Scriptures;
he ascended into heaven
and is seated at the right hand of the Father.
He will come again in glory to judge the
  living and the dead,
and his kingdom will have no end.**

We believe in the Holy Spirit, the Lord, the
    giver of life,
who proceeds from the Father and the Son,
who with the Father and the Son is
    worshipped and glorified,
who has spoken through the prophets.
We believe in one holy catholic and
    apostolic Church.
We acknowledge one Baptism for the
    forgiveness of sins.
We look for the resurrection of the dead,
and the life of the world to come.  **Amen.**

## THE LORD'S SUPPER

### THE PREPARATION OF THE GIFTS

18 Hymn

**19** The offerings of the people are presented.
Bread and wine are brought to the table (or if
already on the table are uncovered).   The
presiding minister takes the bread and wine
and prepares them for use.

20    Lord and Giver of every good thing,
      we bring to you
      bread and wine for our communion,
      lives and gifts for your kingdom,
      all for transformation through your grace
        and love,
      made known in Jesus Christ our Saviour. **Amen.**

### THE PREPARATION OF THE GIFTS

15 Hymn

**16** The offerings of the people are presented.
Bread and wine are brought to the table (or if
already on the table are uncovered).   The
presiding minister takes the bread and wine
and prepares them for use.

### THE PREPARATION OF THE GIFTS

17 Hymn

**18** The offerings of the people are presented.
Bread and wine are brought to the table (or if
already on the table are uncovered).   The
presiding minister takes the bread and wine
and prepares them for use.

# We give thanks

## THE THANKSGIVING

**21** All stand.

The presiding minister leads the great prayer of thanksgiving:

The Lord be with you.
**And also with you.**

Lift up your hearts.
**We lift them to the Lord.**

Let us give thanks to the Lord our God.
**It is right to give our thanks and praise.**

We praise you, gracious Father,
our Maker and Sustainer.
You created the heavens and the earth
and formed us in your own image.
Though we sinned against you,
your love for us was constant,
and you sent your Son Jesus Christ
to be the Saviour of the world.

Sharing our human nature,
he was born of Mary
and baptized in the Jordan.
He proclaimed your kingdom, by word and deed,
and was put to death upon the cross.

## THE THANKSGIVING

**17** All stand.

The presiding minister leads the great prayer of thanksgiving:

The Lord be with you.
**And also with you.**

Lift up your hearts.
**We lift them to the Lord.**

Let us give thanks to the Lord our God.
**It is right to give our thanks and praise.**

God our Father and our Mother,
we give you thanks and praise
for all that you have made,
for the stars in their splendour
and the world in its wonder
and for the glorious gift of human life.
With the saints and angels in heaven
we praise your holy name.

EITHER

A **Holy, holy, holy Lord,
God of power and might,
heaven and earth are full of your glory.
Hosanna in the highest.
Blessèd is he who comes in the name of the Lord.
Hosanna in the highest.**

## THE THANKSGIVING

**19** All stand.

The presiding minister leads the great prayer of thanksgiving:

The Lord be with you.
**And also with you.**

Lift up your hearts.
**We lift them to the Lord.**

Let us give thanks to the Lord our God.
**It is right to give our thanks and praise.**

It is indeed right, always and everywhere,
to give thanks to you, the true and living God.
Endless is your mercy and eternal is your reign.
All creation rejoices in your radiant splendour.

You made a covenant with your people
and declared your purpose of justice and love.
When all things were ready,
you sent your Son to be our Saviour.
In words and deeds he proclaimed your kingdom,
and obeyed your will even to death on the cross.

You raised him from the dead;
you exalted him in glory;
and through him you have sent your Holy Spirit,
calling us to be your people,
a community of faith.

---

### ON TRINITY SUNDAY

And now we give you thanks
because you have revealed your glory
as the glory of your Son and
    of the Holy Spirit:
three persons equal in majesty,
undivided in splendour,
yet one Lord, one God,
ever to be worshipped
(And so . . . )

---

### ON ALL SAINTS DAY (or for any saint)

And now we give you thanks
for the glorious pledge of the hope of
    our calling
which you have given us in your saints;
that, following their example
and strengthened by their fellowship,
we may run with perseverance
the race that is set before us,
and with them receive the unfading
    crown of glory.
(And so . . . )

---

OR

B

Ho - ly, ho - ly, ho - ly is the Lord;
ho - ly is the Lord God al - migh - - - ty!
1.
ty! Who was, and is, and is to come!
2.
Ho - ly ho - ly, ho - ly is the Lord!

---

Holy God, you go on loving us
even when we turn away from you.
You sent your Son Jesus
who healed those who were sick,
wept with those who were sad,
and forgave sinners.
To show the world your love
he died for all upon
    the cross
and you raised him up
    in glory.

Through his mighty resurrection
he overcame sin and death
to set the whole creation free.

Therefore with saints and angels
and with all the choirs of heaven,
we join in the song of eternal praise:

**Holy, holy, holy Lord,**
**God of power and might,**
**heaven and earth are full of your glory.**
**Hosanna in the highest.**
**Blessèd is he who comes in the name of the**
    **Lord.**
**Hosanna in the highest.**

We praise you, Father,
that on the night in which he was betrayed,
our Lord Jesus took bread and gave thanks,
broke it, and gave it to his disciples, saying,
'Take and eat.  This is my body, given for you.
Do this in remembrance of me.'

And so, with angels and archangels
and all the choirs of heaven,
we join in the triumphant hymn:

**Holy, holy, holy Lord,**
**God of power and might,**
**heaven and earth are full of your glory.**
**Hosanna in the highest.**
**Blessèd is he who comes in the name of the**
**  Lord.**
**Hosanna in the highest.**

Holy God, we praise you
that on the night in which he was betrayed
our Saviour Christ took bread
and gave you thanks.
He broke it, and gave it to his disciples,
  saying,
'Take, eat.  This is my body, given for you.
Do this in remembrance of me.'

After supper, he took the cup of wine,
gave thanks, and gave it to them, saying,
'Drink from it, all of you.
This is my blood of the new covenant,
poured out for all people
for the forgiveness of sins.
Do this in remembrance of me.'

On the night before Jesus died,
he had supper with his disciples.
He took bread,
thanked you, as we are thanking you,
broke the bread,
and gave it to them, saying,
'Take, eat. This is my body, given for you.
Do this to remember me.'

After supper, he took a cup of wine,
thanked you,
and gave it to his disciples, saying,
'Drink from it, all of you.
This cup is the new covenant in my blood.
It will be shed for you and for all people
for the forgiveness of sins.
Do this to remember me.'

**Jesus the Lord says, I am the vine,**
**the true and fruitful vine am I.**

And so, God of love,
we remember that Jesus died and rose again
to make all things new.
Through his offering for us all,
we offer our whole life to you in thanks and
  praise.

**Jesus the Lord says, I am the bread,**
**the bread of life for the world am I.**

After supper, he took the cup, gave thanks,
and gave it for all to drink, saying,
'This cup is the new covenant of my blood,
shed for you and for all people
for the forgiveness of sin.
Do this in remembrance of me.'

**As often as we eat this bread and drink this cup**
**we proclaim the Lord's death until he comes.**

Therefore, gracious God,
with this bread and this cup
we remember that our Lord offered his life
  for us.

Believing the witness of his resurrection and
  ascension,
we look for his coming in glory,
and our sharing in his great and promised
  feast.

**Amen.  Come, Lord Jesus.**

Send now, we pray, your Holy Spirit,
that these gifts of bread and wine
may be for us the body and blood of Christ
and that we may live to your praise and glory
with all your saints in light.

**Amen.  Come, Holy Spirit.**

Remembering, therefore, his death and
    resurrection,
and proclaiming his eternal sacrifice,
we offer ourselves to you in praise and
    thanksgiving,
as we declare the mystery of faith:

**Christ has died.**
**Christ is risen.**
**Christ will come again.**

Send down your Holy Spirit
that these gifts of bread and wine
may be for us the body and blood of Christ.
Unite us with him for ever
and bring us with the whole creation
to your eternal kingdom.

**Through Christ, with Christ, in Christ,**
**in the power of the Holy Spirit,**
**we worship you in songs of everlasting**
    **praise.**
**Blessing and honour and glory and power**
**be yours for ever and ever.  Amen.**

Send your Holy Spirit
that these gifts of bread and wine
may be for us Christ's saving body and blood.
May this same Spirit unite us
with all your people on earth and in heaven.

Bring us at last
to live in your glory with all your saints,
that we may praise you for ever,
through Jesus your Son,
in the fellowship of the Holy Spirit.

This or some other doxology ending with **Amen**
is sung or said:

**All glory to the Father be,**
**the Spirit and the Son:**
**all glory to the One in Three**
**while endless ages run.**
**Alleluia!  Amen.**

Join our prayers
and the prayers of all your people
on earth and in heaven
with the intercession of Christ,
our great high priest,

**through whom, with whom, and in whom,**
**in the unity of the Holy Spirit,**
**all worship and honour are yours,**
**almighty God and Father,**
**for ever and ever.  Amen.**

**18** The Lord's Prayer
EITHER

We say together the prayer that Jesus gave us:

**Our Father in heaven,
hallowed be your Name,
your kingdom come,
your will be done,
on earth as in heaven.
Give us today our daily bread.
Forgive us our sins
as we forgive those who sin against us.
Save us from the time of trial
and deliver us from evil.
For the kingdom, the power and
the glory are yours,
now and for ever. Amen.**

OR

As our Saviour taught his disciples, we pray:

**Our Father, who art in heaven,
hallowed be thy Name;
thy kingdom come;
thy will be done;
on earth as it is in heaven.
Give us this day our daily bread.
And forgive us our trespasses,
as we forgive those who trespass against us.
And lead us not into temptation;
but deliver us from evil.
For thine is the kingdom, the power,
and the glory,
for ever and ever. Amen.**

**20** The Lord's Prayer
EITHER

We say together the prayer that Jesus gave us:

**Our Father in heaven,
hallowed be your Name,
your kingdom come,
your will be done,
on earth as in heaven.
Give us today our daily bread.
Forgive us our sins
as we forgive those who sin against us.
Save us from the time of trial
and deliver us from evil.
For the kingdom, the power and
the glory are yours,
now and for ever. Amen.**

OR

As our Saviour taught his disciples, we pray:

**Our Father, who art in heaven,
hallowed be thy Name;
thy kingdom come;
thy will be done;
on earth as it is in heaven.
Give us this day our daily bread.
And forgive us our trespasses,
as we forgive those who trespass against us.
And lead us not into temptation;
but deliver us from evil.
For thine is the kingdom, the power,
and the glory,
for ever and ever. Amen.**

## THE BREAKING OF THE BREAD

**22** The presiding minister breaks the bread in the sight of the people in silence, or saying:

EITHER

We break this bread to share in the body of Christ.

**Though we are many, we are one body, because we all share in one bread.**

OR

The gifts of God for the people of God.
**May Jesus Christ be praised!**

**23** Silence, all seated or kneeling

24 EITHER

A  Jesus, Lamb of God,
**have mercy on us.**
Jesus, bearer of our sins,
**have mercy on us.**
Jesus, redeemer of the world,
**grant us peace.**

OR

B  Jesus is the Lamb of God
who takes away the sin of the world.
Happy are those who are called to his supper.

**Lord, I am not worthy to receive you, but only say the word and I shall be healed.**

## THE BREAKING OF THE BREAD

**19** The presiding minister breaks the bread in the sight of the people in silence, or saying:

The bread we break is a sharing in the body of Christ.
**Christ is the Bread of Life.**

The presiding minister may lift the cup in silence, or saying:

The cup of blessing for which we give thanks is a sharing in the blood of Christ.
**Christ is the True Vine.**

20 Silence, all seated or kneeling

21  Jesus, Lamb of God,
**have mercy on us.**
Jesus, bearer of our sins,
**have mercy on us.**
Jesus, redeemer of the world,
**grant us peace.**

## THE BREAKING OF THE BREAD

**21** The presiding minister breaks the bread in the sight of the people in silence, or saying:

The bread we break is a sharing in the body of Christ.
**Christ is the Bread of Life.**

The presiding minister may lift the cup in silence, or saying:

The cup we take is a sharing in the blood of Christ.
**Christ is the True Vine.**

**22** Silence, all seated or kneeling

23 *Lamb of God* or some other short hymn or song on a similar theme

Jesus, Lamb of God,
**have mercy on us.**
Jesus, bearer of our sins,
**have mercy on us.**
Jesus, redeemer of the world,
**grant us peace.**

OR

Let us pray.

**C** **We do not presume**
**to come to this your table, merciful Lord,**
**trusting in our own righteousness,**
**but in your manifold and great mercies.**
**We are not worthy**
**so much as to gather up the crumbs under**
**your table.**
**But you are the same Lord**
**whose nature is always to have mercy.**
**Grant us therefore, gracious Lord,**
**so to eat the flesh of your dear Son Jesus**
**Christ**
**and to drink his blood,**

**that we may evermore dwell in him**
**and he in us. Amen.**

OR

We say together:

**D** **Lord, we come to your table,**
**trusting in your mercy**
**and not in any goodness of our own.**
**We are not worthy**
**even to gather up the crumbs under your table,**
**but it is your nature always to have mercy,**
**and on that we depend.**
**So feed us with the body and blood**
**of Jesus Christ, your Son,**
**that we may for ever live in him**
**and he in us. Amen.**

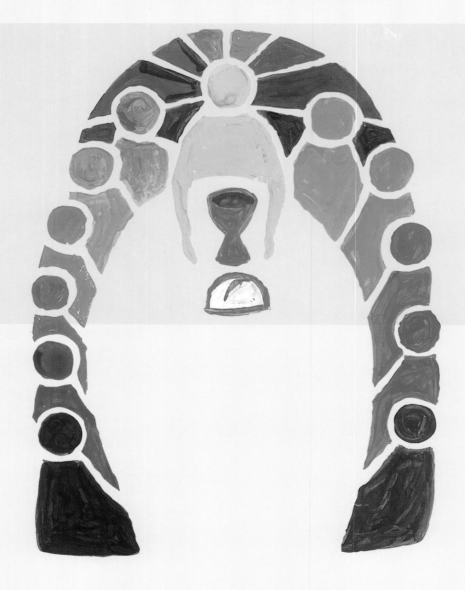

THE SHARING OF THE BREAD AND WINE

**25** The presiding minister, those assisting with the distribution, and the people receive, according to local custom.

The presiding minister may say these or other words of invitation:

Jesus said: 'I am the bread of life.
Those who come to me shall not hunger
and those who believe in me shall never
   thirst.'

Draw near with faith.

**26** Words such as the following are said during the distribution:

The body of Christ keep you in eternal life.
   **Amen.**

The blood of Christ keep you in eternal life.
   **Amen.**

**27** During the distribution there may be appropriate music.

**28** The elements that remain are covered with a white cloth.

THE SHARING OF THE BREAD AND WINE

**22** The presiding minister, those assisting with the distribution, and the people receive, according to local custom.

Appropriate words of invitation may be said.

**23** Words such as the following are said during the distribution:

The body of Christ, given for you.  **Amen.**

The blood of Christ, shed for you.  **Amen.**

**24** During the distribution there may be appropriate music.

**25** The elements that remain are covered with a white cloth.

THE SHARING OF THE BREAD AND WINE

**24** The presiding minister, those assisting with the distribution, and the people receive, according to local custom.

The presiding minister may say these or other words of invitation:

Jesus is the Lamb of God
who takes away the sin of the world.
Happy are those who are called to his supper.

Receive the body of Christ which was given
   for you
and the blood of Christ which was shed for
   you,

and feed on him in your hearts,
by faith with thanksgiving.

**25** Words such as the following are said during the distribution:

The body of Christ.  **Amen.**

The blood of Christ.  **Amen.**

**26** During the distribution there may be appropriate music.

**27** The elements that remain are covered with a white cloth.

PRAYERS AND DISMISSAL

29 Silence

30 Let us pray.

**We thank you, Lord,
that you have fed us in this sacrament,
united us with Christ,
and given us a foretaste of the heavenly
      banquet
prepared for all people.  Amen.**

31 This or some other hymn:

**Love's redeeming work is done,
      Alleluia!
Fought the fight, the battle won;
      Alleluia!
Vain the stone, the watch, the seal;
      Alleluia!
Christ has burst the gates of hell;
      Alleluia!**

PRAYERS AND DISMISSAL

26 Silence

27 Let us pray.

**God of glory,
we have seen with our eyes
and touched with our hands
the bread of heaven.
Strengthen us in our life together
that we may grow in love
for you and for each other;
through Jesus Christ our Lord.  Amen.**

28 Hymn

29 The presiding minister says:

The blessing of God,
the Father, the Son and the Holy Spirit,
be upon *you/us*, now and always.  **Amen.**

**30** The presiding minister says:

Go in peace to love and serve the Lord.

**In the name of Christ.  Amen.**

PRAYERS AND DISMISSAL

28 Silence

29 Let us pray.

**We praise you, God,
for the bread of heaven
and the cup of salvation
which you give for the life of the world.
With this food for our journey
bring us with your saints
to the feast of your glory. Amen.**

30 Hymn

31 The presiding minister says:

EITHER

The Lord bless you and keep you;
the Lord make his face to shine on you
and be gracious to you;
the Lord look on you with kindness
and give you peace.  **Amen.**

OR

God be gracious to us and bless us,
and make his face to shine upon us.  **Amen.**

Soar we now where Christ has led,
    Alleluia!
Following our exalted Head;
    Alleluia!
Made like him, like him we rise;
    Alleluia!
Ours the cross, the grave, the skies;
    Alleluia!

**32** The presiding minister says:

The blessing of God,
the Father, the Son and the Holy Spirit,
remain with *you/us* always.  **Amen.**

**33** The presiding minister says:

Go in peace in the power of the Spirit
to live and work to God's praise and glory.

**Thanks be to God.  Amen.**

**32** The presiding minister says:

Go in peace to love and serve the Lord.
**In the name of Christ.  Amen.**

# ACKNOWLEDGEMENTS

Every effort has been made to ensure that the following list of acknowledgements is as comprehensive as possible, but the experience of those involved in the preparation of **The Methodist Worship Book** is similar to that of the compilers of the **Book of Common Order** of the Church of Scotland, who state:

> Many sources have contributed to the compilation of this book, and not all of them are now traceable. Individual members of the Committee prepared drafts, which were revised more or less drastically by the Committee, often resulting in final versions which looked little like the original drafts. Among the casualties of this sometimes protracted process was the identity of many of the sources; they could not be recalled, nor did there seem to be any way to track them down. The Panel wishes to record at once both its indebtedness to any who may recognise in this book rhythms and patterns, expressions and phrases, ideas and images which are their own, and its regret that it became impossible to ask permission or seek consent for their inclusion . . .

If, through inadvertence, copyright material has been used without permission or acknowledgement, the publisher will be grateful to be informed and will be pleased to make the necessary correction in subsequent editions.

The symbol * in the following paragraphs denotes that a text has been altered.

Except where indicated below, all psalms, scripture readings and scripture sentences are taken from **The New Revised Standard Version of the Bible (Anglicized Edition)**, © 1989, 1995 by the Division of Christian Education of the National Council of Churches of Christ in the United States of America, and are used by permission. All rights reserved.

Some scripture sentences are from **The Revised Standard Version**, © 1946 and 1952 by the Division of Christian Education of the National Council of Churches of Christ in the United States of America, and are used by permission. All rights reserved.

Some scripture sentences are from **The Revised English Bible**, © 1989 Oxford University Press and Cambridge University Press.

One scripture sentence comes from **The New Jerusalem Bible**, © 1985 Darton Longman & Todd and Doubleday & Co. Inc.

The texts of *Glory to God in the highest*, the Nicene Creed, the Apostles' Creed, *Sursum Corda*, *Sanctus*, *Benedictus Qui Venit*, *Gloria Patri*, *Te Deum Laudamus*, *Benedictus*, *Magnificat*, and the left hand column version of the Lord's Prayer are from **Praying Together**, © 1988 by the English Language Liturgical Commission (ELLC).

> The text of *Agnus Dei* is also from *Praying Together*. After the initial publication of *the Methodist Worship Book* it was discovered that the text of *Benedictus* (pages 4f) as approved by the Conference differed from the ELLC text in the following respect: line 20 of *Benedictus* should read 'on high' not 'heaven'. This error is regretted but the text as approved by the Conference and printed in this and all previous editions has been left uncorrected.

# Letts
## gets you through

C000131565

# KS2 SCIENCE
# SUCCESS
## REVISION AND PRACTICE

# KS2 SCIENCE

## REVISION AND PRACTICE

# PHILIPPA HULME

# REVISION GUIDE

# WORKBOOK

Listen up 1

## Why classify?

There is a huge variety of living things. Scientists **classify** them into groups so they can find out more about them. The living things in each group have similar features.

**For example:**

This gecko is an animal.    This sunflower is a plant.

## The three main groups

Every living thing is in one of three broad groups. The groups are:

- **animals**, which eat other living things
- **plants**, which make their own food
- **microorganisms**, which are tiny living things that you can only see with a microscope.

### Animals

Scientists divide **animals** into two big groups. They are:

- **vertebrates**, which have bony skeletons, including backbones
- **invertebrates**, which do not have backbones.

Each of these groups is sub-divided into smaller groups. The table shows the five groups of **vertebrates**.

| Group | Characteristics | Example |
|---|---|---|
| amphibians | damp skin, lay eggs in water | |
| reptiles | dry, scaly skin | |
| fish | scaly skin, fins, breathe underwater | |
| birds | feathers, wings, lay eggs | |
| mammals | hairy, live young, feed their young milk | |

# The three main groups (continued)

There are several groups of **invertebrates**. These include:

- worms
- animals with shells, such as snails
- arthropods, including insects and spiders.

### Plants

Scientists divide **plants** into two big groups. They are:

- **flowering plants**, including grasses
- **non-flowering plants**, such as mosses, ferns and conifer trees.

**Parent tip!**

When your child finds an invertebrate, encourage them to observe it closely and to count its legs and wings (if it has any!). Make sure they care for it and return it safely to where it was found, or to a similar place.

## Working scientifically

**Classification keys**

Riana makes a **classification key** to identify five invertebrates. She shows Dan how to use the key to identify an animal he has found at school.

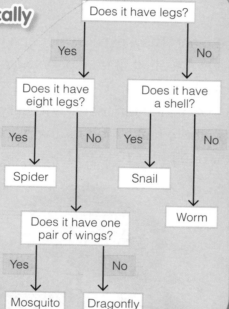

Does it have legs?
- Yes → Does it have eight legs?
  - Yes → Spider
  - No → Does it have one pair of wings?
    - Yes → Mosquito
    - No → Dragonfly
- No → Does it have a shell?
  - Yes → Snail
  - No → Worm

## Keywords

**Classify** ➤ To sort living things into groups depending on their similarities and differences

**Vertebrate** ➤ An animal with a bony skeleton and backbone

**Invertebrate** ➤ An animal without a backbone

**Classification key** ➤ A series of questions to help you identify a living thing

**Have a go!**

Go outside and find as many different types of invertebrate as possible.

- ➤ Classify them into groups depending on their number of legs, or whether they have a shell, or how many pairs of wings they have.
- ➤ Draw pictures of your invertebrates in their groups.

**Test yourself**

1. What do all plants have in common?
2. What is a vertebrate?
3. Name the five vertebrate groups.
4. Name two types of arthropod.
5. Look at the image and the classification key in the Working scientifically box. Use the key to identify Dan's animal.

## What plants need

To live and grow, plants need:
- air, water and **nutrients**
- light and space.

Not all plants have the same needs. For example, pineapples grow in warmer places than apples. Pineapple plants grow very slowly (and can even die) if it is too cold.

## Plant parts

Each part of a plant has its own job.
- The **roots** support the plant. They take in water and nutrients from the soil.
- The **stem** also supports the plant. It transports water and nutrients from the roots to the leaves and flowers.
- **Leaves** take in carbon dioxide from the air. When it is light they use carbon dioxide and water to make food for the plant.
- **Flowers** make seeds. See page 10 to find out more.

Both the roots and stem transport water to the leaves and flowers.

Top tip!

flower

stem

leaf

roots

Listen up 2

## Working scientifically

### Stem transport

Jamal wants to find out how water gets to a flower. He has two white flowers. He puts one white flower in a glass of normal water. He puts red food colouring in a second glass of water and adds the other white flower. Jamal writes his observations in a table.

| Water colour | Observations |
|---|---|
| normal | The flower remains white. |
| red | The flower goes red. |

Jamal uses his observations to make a prediction:

If I put a white flower in blue water, the flower will go blue.

Jamal tests his prediction. He is correct. His teacher helps him to write a conclusion:

Tubes in the stem carry water to the flower.

## Keyword

**Nutrient** ➤ A substance that a plant or animal needs to survive, grow and stay healthy

**Have a go!** Put one stick of celery in normal water and another in a mixture of food colouring and water. Make careful observations and write them down.

**Test yourself**

1. List five things that plants need.
2. What is the job of a flower in a plant?
3. Name two parts of a plant that support it.
4. Describe two things that happen in leaves.

## Metamorphosis

All living things change as they grow. Some change completely and the young look nothing like the adult. This is **metamorphosis**.

### Frog

A frog is an amphibian. It starts life as an egg in a blob of jelly (frog spawn). It emerges as a tadpole, which gradually changes into a tiny frog.

### Butterfly

A butterfly is an insect. It starts life as a tiny egg. A caterpillar (**larva**) comes out of the egg. It feeds and grows.

The caterpillar forms a chrysalis (**pupa**). Inside the chrysalis an adult butterfly is forming. Later, the butterfly emerges. If it is female it mates with a male butterfly and lays eggs. The cycle starts again.

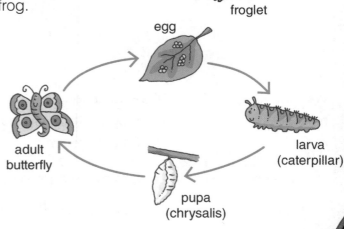

frog spawn

tadpole

froglet

adult frog

egg

larva (caterpillar)

pupa (chrysalis)

adult butterfly

## Bird life cycle

A chicken is a bird. Like all birds, a female chicken lays eggs. If the female has mated with a male, a chick develops inside each egg. A few weeks later, the egg hatches. The chick that comes out grows into an adult chicken.

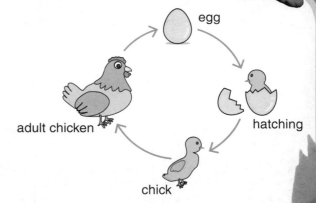

egg

hatching

chick

adult chicken

**Top tip!**

One way to remember the word **metamorphosis** is to think about something in a film or video game that changes into something completely different – by morphing.

# Mammal life cycle

Humans are mammals.
You started life as a foetus inside your mum.
You were born as a helpless **baby** and grew into
a **toddler** and then a **child**. During **puberty** your
body changes as you move towards **adulthood**.

The table shows some of the changes that take
place during puberty.

| Boys | Girls |
| --- | --- |
| body hair grows | body hair grows |
| penis gets bigger | breasts grow |
| shoulders widen | hips widen |
| voice deepens | periods start |

## Keywords

**Metamorphosis** ➤ When an
animal changes completely as
it grows
**Larva** ➤ The young of an animal
that hatches from an egg. It is
very different from the adult
**Pupa** ➤ The third stage in the
life cycle of some insects
**Puberty** ➤ The stage of life when
a child's body matures to become
an adult

Listen up
**3**

**Have
a go!**
Search 'metamorphosis'
on the Internet. List
some animals that
metamorphose as
they grow. Make a file
of photographs of
animals at different
stages of their life
cycles.

**Test
yourself**

❶ Explain what
metamorphosis means.
❷ Name one insect and
one amphibian that
metamorphose.
❸ Put these stages for the
life cycle of a frog in the
correct order:

> froglet          frog
> tadpole        frog spawn

❹ List the four stages of the
life cycle of a butterfly.

## Life goes on

All living things produce young, or reproduce. Most animals, and many plants, reproduce by **sexual reproduction**.

Listen up 4

## New plants

Sexual reproduction in flowering plants involves making seeds.

1. Insects, or the wind, take pollen from the stamen of one flower to the stigma of another. This is **pollination**. Sometimes the pollen lands on the stigma of the same flower. This is self-pollination.

2. Pollen moves down to the ovary. Here, it joins with ovules to make seeds. This is **fertilisation**.

3. Seeds move away from the plant. The wind disperses some seeds. Other seeds are inside fruit. Animals eat the fruit. The seeds come out in their faeces (poo).

4. Seeds grow into new plants.

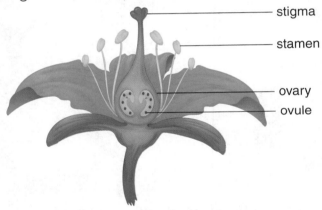

- stigma
- stamen
- ovary
- ovule

Some plants reproduce without seeds. This is **asexual reproduction**. It needs only one parent. The young are identical to their parents.

- **Strawberries** have runners. New plants grow from the runners.
- **Daffodils** make bulbs which develop into new plants.

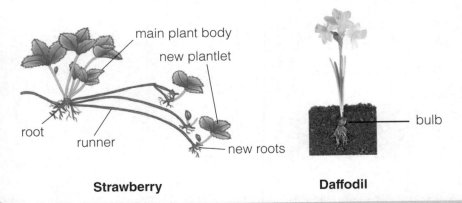

main plant body
new plantlet
root
runner
new roots
bulb

**Strawberry**                    **Daffodil**

# New animals

Most animals, including humans, make their young by **sexual reproduction**. Sperm from the father joins with an egg from the mother. This is **fertilisation**.

In mammals, the fertilised egg forms a foetus inside the mother. The foetus develops and a baby animal is born.

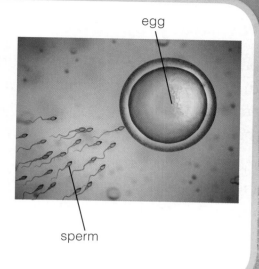

egg

sperm

## Keywords

**Sexual reproduction** ➤ Making a new living thing by joining pollen with an ovule (in plants) or a sperm with an egg (in animals)

**Pollination** ➤ The transport of pollen from one flower to another

**Fertilisation** ➤ The joining of pollen with ovules to make seeds in plants, or the joining of a sperm with an egg in animals

**Asexual reproduction** ➤ Making a new plant without seeds

**Parent tip!** Ask your child to explain how flowers make seeds.

**Have a go!** Carefully use scissors or a knife to cut open a flower; for example, a lily, daffodil or fuchsia (ask an adult to help you). Can you find its stamens, stigma and ovaries? Afterwards, wash your hands carefully.

**Test yourself**

❶ What is reproduction?

❷ A blackberry plant is produced by asexual reproduction. How many parent plants does it have?

❸ Describe one difference between pollination and fertilisation in plants.

❹ Holly seeds are inside red berries. Describe how a bird would disperse holly seeds.

## Circulatory system

All parts of your body need nutrients (from food) and oxygen. Your **circulatory system** takes nutrients and oxygen to where they are needed. It also carries waste away.

Your circulatory system includes your heart, blood vessels and blood.

- Your **heart** is a strong muscle. It pumps blood around your body. It beats about 70 times every minute.
- Your **blood** is mainly water. Nutrients dissolve in the water. Blood also includes red blood cells to carry oxygen.
- Blood travels through tubes called **blood vessels**.

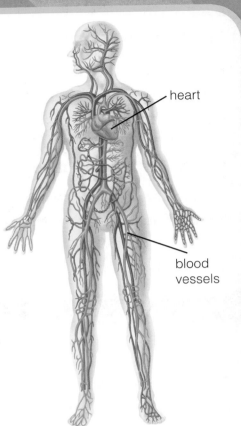

heart

blood vessels

**Where blood enters and leaves the heart**

blood leaves the heart

blood enters the heart

blood enters the heart

## Blood vessels

There are different types of blood vessel, including arteries and veins. **Arteries** carry blood away from your heart to all other parts of your body. **Veins** return blood to the heart. The diagram of the circulatory system above shows arteries in red and veins in purple.

One artery joins your heart to your brain. It carries blood that is rich in oxygen and nutrients. Your brain removes the oxygen and nutrients that it needs. It replaces them with waste substances. The blood takes this waste away.

## Working scientifically

### Measuring pulse rates

Your pulse measures how fast your heart is beating. Cora measures her pulse after resting, walking and jogging, by placing her fingers gently on her neck. She writes her results in a table.

| Activity | Pulse rate after activity (beats per minute) |
|----------|----------------------------------------------|
| resting | 80 |
| walking | 100 |
| jogging | 150 |

The results show that Cora's heart beats faster after exercise.

## Keywords

**Circulatory system** ➤ The circulatory system includes the heart, blood vessels and blood. It transports nutrients and oxygen around the body

**Heart** ➤ The heart pumps blood around the body

**Blood** ➤ Blood is mainly water with dissolved nutrients. It also includes red blood cells

**Blood vessels** ➤ The tubes that blood flows through

**Top tip!** Remember, **a**rteries carry blood **away** from the heart.

**Have a go!** Sit still for a minute and then measure your pulse rate. Then run around for a minute and measure your pulse rate again. Is there any change? If so, can you explain what might cause this?

**Test yourself**

❶ Name the three parts of the circulatory system.

❷ What does your heart do?

❸ Name two substances that are transported in the blood.

❹ Look at the table in the Working scientifically box above. Predict what Cora's pulse rate might be after running fast.

## Skeletons

Imagine having no bones. What would your body be like?

Humans have hard **skeletons** inside their bodies. So do all other mammals, as well as birds, fish, amphibians and reptiles. Your skeleton is made up of more than 200 bones.

Your skeleton has three main jobs.

- **It supports you** – it holds you upright.
- **It protects you** – e.g. your ribs protect your heart and lungs, and your skull protects your brain.
- **It helps you to move** – e.g. your skeleton bends at your knees and elbows, where bones meet and join.

skull

ribs

## Muscles

You have more than 350 **muscles** in your body, including your heart. Your muscles work with your skeleton to help you move.

Muscles are joined to bones. When a muscle **contracts**, it gets shorter and fatter. It pulls up the bone it is joined to. When the muscle **relaxes**, it goes back to its original shape.

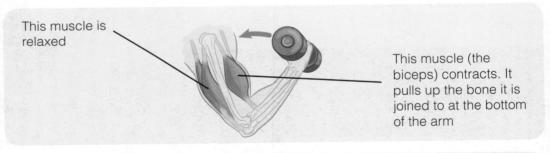

This muscle is relaxed

This muscle (the biceps) contracts. It pulls up the bone it is joined to at the bottom of the arm

This muscle contracts to pull down the bone it is joined to at the bottom of the arm

This muscle is now relaxed

## Working scientifically

### Comparing skeletons

Emma has two X-ray images. They show cat and snake bones.
She compares the X-rays and writes down her observations.

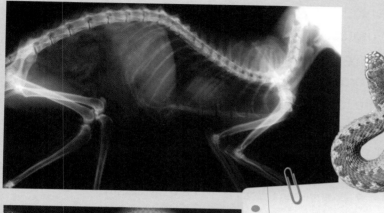

Both animals have a backbone and ribs.

The snake has more ribs.

Listen up 6

### Keywords

**Skeleton** ➤ The structure of bones in a body
**Muscles** ➤ Muscles help animals to move
**Contract** ➤ When a muscle contracts, it becomes short and fat
**Relax** ➤ When a muscle relaxes, it returns to its original shape

**Parent tip!**

Ask your child to tell you why their skeleton is important.

**Have a go!**

Bend your arm, then straighten it. Can you feel your biceps contract and relax?

**Test yourself**

1. What is a skeleton?
2. A skeleton has three main jobs – what are they?
3. Name five animals that have skeletons inside their bodies.
4. Explain how your muscles help your arm to bend.

**Your Body** | Skeletons and muscles    **15**

## Balanced diet

Plants make their own food but animals cannot.
Animals, including humans, get their nutrients by eating.

There are different types of nutrients.

- **Carbohydrates** are an energy source. Bread, potatoes and pasta are examples of carbohydrates.
- **Fats** also provide energy. Butter, margarine and cooking oil provide fat.
- You need **proteins** for growth. They repair damage to your body. Meat, fish, milk and beans are full of protein.
- Fruit and vegetables provide **vitamins and minerals** to keep your body working properly. For example, vitamin D and calcium help make strong bones.

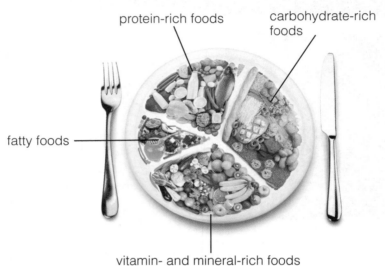

protein-rich foods

carbohydrate-rich foods

fatty foods

vitamin- and mineral-rich foods

To stay healthy you need all these nutrients in the correct amounts. Too much fatty food damages your heart. Too little vitamin D may cause rickets.

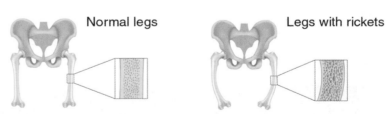

Normal legs

Legs with rickets

## Exercise

You need daily exercise for a healthy heart and strong muscles. Exercise can make you happy and help you to concentrate. If you do not exercise enough, or if you eat too much, you might get fat.

## Drugs and smoking

**Drugs** affect how your body works. Some drugs are medicines. They cure illnesses or make you feel better. Other drugs, such as cannabis and ecstasy, damage your body and mind.

**Alcohol** is the drug in beer and wine. If you have too much, it damages many parts of the body, including the heart, stomach, brain and liver. Too much can kill.

**Tobacco** is the drug in cigarettes. It causes breathing problems, cancer and heart attacks. Over time, smoking kills people.

### Keywords

**Carbohydrates** ➤ Nutrients that provide energy

**Fats** ➤ Nutrients that provide energy. Your body can store them

**Proteins** ➤ Nutrients needed for growth and repair

**Vitamins and minerals** ➤ Nutrients that keep your body working properly

**Drugs** ➤ Substances that affect how your body works

Help your child to understand the differences between medicinal drugs and recreational drugs.

**Parent tip!**

**Have a go!**

Read labels on food packets to find out which nutrients they contain. Are you surprised at what the labels say?

**Test yourself**

1. Name four different types of nutrients.
2. Name two foods that are high in fat.
3. Name four parts of the body that are damaged by alcohol.
4. Name two drugs that adults can buy at the shops but that can also kill.

# Digestive system

Your body cannot use the food you eat just as it is.
Your **digestive system** breaks down food so that your body can absorb it.

**1** In your **mouth**, your **tongue** detects tastes and your **teeth** chew food. Chemicals in your saliva start to break down the food.

**2** Chewed food travels down the **oesophagus**.

**3** In your **stomach**, chewed food mixes with digestive juices. The food starts to break down.

**4** Partly digested food enters your **small intestine**. Extra digestive juices break down the food even more. Digested food passes through the intestine walls, into your blood.

**5** Food that cannot be digested enters your **large intestine**. Here, water passes into your blood.

**6** Your **rectum** holds undigested food as faeces (poo).

**7** Faeces leave your body through your **anus**.

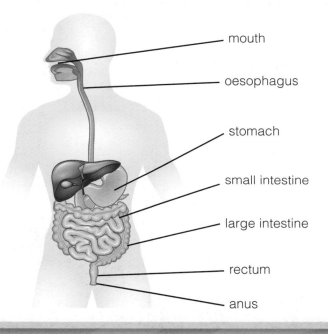

mouth

oesophagus

stomach

small intestine

large intestine

rectum

anus

## Keywords

**Digestive system** ➤ Your digestive system breaks down food so that your body can use it

**Oesophagus** ➤ Chewed food passes down this tube from the mouth to the stomach

**Stomach** ➤ Digestive juices start to digest food here

**Small intestine** ➤ Digested food passes into the blood from here

**Large intestine** ➤ Water from undigested food passes into the body from here

# Teeth

Teeth are an important part of the digestive system.
The three types of teeth are:

- **incisors**, which bite off pieces of food
- **canines**, which are pointed for tearing food
- **molars**, which grind and chew.

Humans have two sets of teeth:
20 milk teeth as a child, and later
32 permanent teeth.

It is important to look after your teeth by:

- avoiding sugary food and drinks
- brushing them twice a day
- going to the dentist for check-ups.

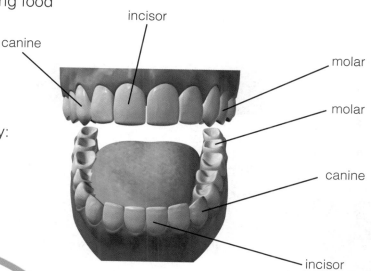

canine
incisor
molar
molar
canine
incisor

One way to remember the order of the parts of the digestive system is MOSSLRA: **m**outh, **o**esophagus, **s**tomach, **s**mall intestine, **l**arge intestine, **r**ectum, **a**nus.

Top tip!

Listen up
8

Have a go!

Use the Internet to find out how the teeth of a predator, such as a wolf, are different from the teeth of a grazing animal, such as a sheep. Can you explain these differences?

Test yourself

1 What is the job of the digestive system?

2 What happens in the stomach?

3 What are the three main ways of looking after your teeth?

4 Describe one difference in the appearance of incisors and molars. Give a reason for this difference.

# What eats what?

Plants make their own food but animals do not. Instead, animals eat other living things.

**Food chains** show how animals get the nutrients they need.

Here is a food chain.

clover ➡ snail ➡ hedgehog ➡ badger

Most food chains start with green plants, such as clover. Green plants are **producers**.

The arrows mean 'is eaten by'. In this food chain the clover is eaten by the snail, the snail is eaten by the hedgehog and the hedgehog is eaten by the badger.

Animals that eat other animals are **predators**. Hedgehogs and badgers are predators.

The hedgehog is also a **prey** animal. It is eaten by other animals, for example the badger. The food chain shows that snails are the prey of hedgehogs.

Changes to one plant or animal in a food chain affect other parts of the chain. For example, if badgers are killed the number of hedgehogs might increase.

## Keywords

**Food chain** ➤ A diagram that shows what eats what
**Producer** ➤ A living thing that makes its own food. Plants are producers
**Predator** ➤ An animal that eats other animals
**Prey** ➤ An animal that is eaten by other animals

Listen up
9

# Another snail food chain

Most animals belong to many food chains.
Here is another food chain that includes snails.

nettle  snail  frog  heron

**Parent tip!**

Reinforce the meanings of the words **producer**, **predator** and **prey** when you see plants and animals. Encourage your child to draw food chains that include the living things you see.

Use the Internet to find examples of food chains. What do you notice about how they are set out?

**Test yourself**

❶ What is a producer?

❷ Look at the food chain above that includes a heron.

a  Name two prey animals in this food chain.

b  Which animal is both predator and prey?

❸ Draw a food chain involving a zebra, grass and a lion.

## What is an environment?

The **environment** of a plant or animal is the surroundings that it lives in. The environment provides everything that the plant or animal needs. It might also pose dangers.

## Producer problem: a case study

Judy had grass in front of her house. Caterpillars and slugs lived in this environment.

The animals were part of many food chains. Here are some examples:

grass → caterpillar → blue tit

grass → slug → thrush

grass → caterpillar → frog → fox

Then Judy wanted somewhere to park her car. She dug up the lawn and paved it over.

The slugs and caterpillars had no grass to eat. Some of them died. Some moved away to find food elsewhere. The blue tits and thrushes had no slugs or caterpillars to eat. They died or moved away.

Removing the grass changed the environment. The environment no longer supplied what the animals needed.

## Polar perils

**Climate change** makes arctic ice melt. This makes the environment less suitable for polar bears.

- There is less ice, so it is harder for polar bears to hunt and find prey animals such as seals.
- Distances between sea ice platforms are greater. Swimming between them is more dangerous.

Changes to the environment threaten the survival of polar bears.

### Keyword

**Environment** ➤ The surroundings of a plant or animal. It supplies everything the plant or animal needs

**Top tip!** You can use food chains to help you predict what might happen if the environment changes.

## Change for the better

Some environmental changes benefit living things, including nature reserves and garden ponds.

For example, the pond in the picture provides a perfect environment for newts.

 **Have a go!** Use the Internet to find out how climate change has affected birds. Tell someone else what you have found out.

 **Test yourself**

1. What does the word environment mean?
2. Look again at the case study on page 22. Predict what will happen to the number of foxes around Judy's house.
3. Explain why climate change is making the arctic environment less suitable for polar bears.

## Adaptation

Every plant and animal has features that help it to survive in its environment. These features are **adaptations**.

**For example:**
- polar bears have a thick layer of fat to keep them warm
- meerkats have dark patches around their eyes to protect against the glare of the Sun.

## Variation

The children in your class are not identical. They have different-coloured eyes and different-sized feet. The difference between individuals is called **variation**.

Living things produce **offspring** of the same kind as themselves. For example, cats give birth to cats and humans give birth to humans. However, offspring of the same parents show variation. They are not usually identical to each other or their parents.

### Keywords

**Adaptations** ➤ The features of an animal or plant that help it to survive in its environment

**Variation** ➤ The differences between animals or plants of the same type

**Offspring** ➤ The plants or animals that are produced by their parent or parents

# Evolution

The animals and plants that lived many years ago are not the same as today. They have developed as a result of **evolution**.

This is how giraffes evolved.

1. The earliest giraffes had short necks.
2. By **natural variation**, some had slightly longer necks. They could eat leaves from higher branches. These giraffes were better adapted to their environment.
3. The better adapted longer-necked giraffes survived. The less well-adapted ones died. This is called the **survival of the fittest**.
4. The offspring of longer-necked giraffes were more likely to have longer necks.
5. Steps 2 to 4 happened again and again. Over many years, giraffes' necks became longer.

Charles Darwin played an important role in discovering and explaining evolution. He gathered evidence from detailed observations, many of which he made on a five-year voyage on a ship called *HMS Beagle*. He published his ideas in 1859, in a book called *On the Origin of Species*.

**Top tip!** Giraffes did not get their long necks by stretching!

**Keyword**

Evolution ➤ The development of plants or animals over many years

Use the Internet to find out about the evolution of your favourite animal.
**Have a go!**

**Test yourself**

1. Describe how you show variation from your friends.
2. The eagle is a predator – it eats small mammals and birds. Describe how an eagle is adapted to catch its prey.

3. What does the word offspring mean?
4. Explain what evolution is.

## Rock properties

There are many types of rock. Each has its own properties.

- Rocks can be **soft** or **hard**. It is easy to scratch a soft rock. It is difficult to scratch a hard rock.
- Rocks can be **porous** or **non-porous**. Water can soak into a porous rock, and some rocks are more porous than others. Water cannot soak into a non-porous rock.

Chalk is **soft** and **porous**:

Granite is **hard** and **non-porous**:

## Crystals or grains?

Some types of rock are made up of **crystals**. There are no gaps between the crystals. These rocks are often **hard** and **non-porous**.

Some types of rock, such as chalk, are made up of **grains**. There are gaps between the grains. These rocks are **porous** and **soft**.

### Keywords

**Porous** ➤ Water can soak into a porous material

**Crystal** ➤ A piece of solid material with a regular shape and flat faces

**Grain** ➤ A small piece of a solid material that does not have a regular shape

Listen up
12

**Parent tip!**

Help your child to group rocks depending on their appearance or properties. For example, are they porous or non-porous? Are they hard or soft?

## Fossils

Rocks that are made up of grains may contain **fossils**. A fossil is the remains, or traces, of a plant or animal that lived long ago. Remains include the bones, teeth or shells of animals, and wood from trees. Traces include animal footprints, or even faeces (poo!).

Here is how a fish fossil may form:

1 The fish dies and sinks quickly to the seabed.
2 Its soft body parts decay.
3 Layers of sand bury the hard body parts.
4 Over many years the hard parts form fossils.

Only a few individual animals or plants form fossils when they die. For example, most Tyrannosaurus rex dinosaurs did not form fossils, but a small number of them did. This is because many decay completely before they are buried, or are eaten. Some die in places where they could not be buried.

Fossils provide information about living things from long ago. They are evidence for evolution.

## Soil

Soil is a mixture of **tiny pieces of rock, dead plants** and **dead animals**. It also includes **air** and **water**.

Different soils have different amounts of these things, and are suitable for different plants.

## Keyword

Fossil ➤ The preserved remains or traces of an animal or plant that lived many years ago

**Have a go!** Outside, find as many different types of rock as you can. Look at them through a magnifying glass and draw what you see.

**Test yourself**

1 What is a fossil?
2 What is a porous rock?
3 Name the things that are mixed together in soil.
4 Do you think granite is made up of grains or crystals? Explain why.

# The three states of matter

The different types of 'stuff' that things are made from are called **materials**. Materials can exist in different forms – as **solids**, **liquids** or **gases**. These are the **states of matter**.

One example of a material that can exist in different forms is water.

| solid water (ice) | liquid water | water as a gas |

The properties of a material depend on whether it is in its **solid**, **liquid** or **gas** state.

| State | Shape | Can you hold it? | Can you squash it? | Does it flow and can you pour it? |
|-------|-------|------------------|--------------------|-----------------------------------|
| **solid** | does not change unless you apply a force | yes | no | no |
| **liquid** | takes the shape of the bottom of the container it is in | not easily | no | yes |
| **gas** | fills up its whole container | no | yes | yes |

**Top tip!**

It is not always easy to classify a material as a solid, liquid or gas. For example, you can pour sand from a bucket, but it is not a liquid or gas. You have to think about the separate grains of sand. Each individual grain is a small piece of solid.

## Keywords

**States of matter** ➤ The three forms that matter exists in – solid, liquid and gas

**Melting** ➤ The change of state from solid to liquid

**Freezing** ➤ The change of state from liquid to solid

**Conclusion** ➤ What you have found out in an investigation

Listen up 13

# Changing state

Imagine a piece of solid chocolate in your hand. It warms up and becomes liquid. This is **melting**. When liquid chocolate cools it becomes solid. This is **freezing**. Melting and freezing are **reversible changes**. It is easy to get back what you started with.

Different materials melt at different temperatures.

You can use a thermometer to measure melting temperatures.

**Melting chocolate**

thermometer

bowl

chocolate

bowl

hot water

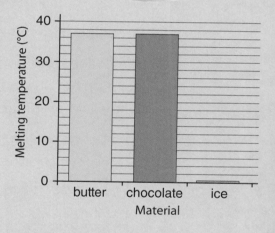

## Working scientifically

**Melting temperatures**

You can use results to make **conclusions**.

Sarah measures the melting temperatures of butter, chocolate and ice. She presents her results in a bar chart.

Sarah uses her results to write a conclusion:

The butter and chocolate both melted at 37 °C. The ice melted at a lower temperature, at around 0 °C.

**Have a go!**

At home, find some materials in the solid, liquid and gas states. Write down their names and which states they are in.

Hint: You cannot see most gases but they are all around you. You can smell some gases.

**Test yourself**

1. Name the three states of matter.

2. Name the change of state when a material changes from solid to liquid.

3. Describe two differences between a material in its solid and liquid states.

## Evaporating and condensing

On a warm day, a puddle disappears. The liquid water has formed water vapour. **Water vapour** is water in the gas state. The change of state from liquid to gas is called **evaporating**. Most liquids evaporate when they are heated.

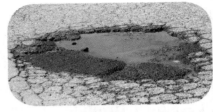

There is water vapour in the air. When water vapour hits a cold surface, like the inside of a window, it becomes liquid. The change from gas to liquid is called **condensing**. Most gases condense when they are cooled.

Evaporating and condensing are **reversible changes**.

### Working scientifically

**Speeding up evaporation**

Ben notices that puddles disappear faster on hot or windy days. He makes two **predictions**:

Water evaporates faster at higher temperatures.

Water evaporates faster in moving air.

Ben does two experiments. He finds out that his predictions are correct:

- The higher the temperature, the faster water evaporates.
- The faster the air is moving, the faster water evaporates.

### Keywords

**Evaporate** ➤ The change of state from liquid to gas

**Condense** ➤ The change of state from gas to liquid

**Prediction** ➤ What you expect to happen in an investigation, based on something you already know or have observed

Top tip!

Remember that e**vap**orating makes water **vap**our. Water vapour is water in the gas state.

Listen up 14

# The water cycle

The **water cycle** describes the movement of water on Earth.

A number of processes are involved in the water cycle.

**1** The Sun heats liquid water on land and in rivers, lakes and seas. Some evaporates, forming water vapour.

**2** Water vapour cools as it rises. It condenses into tiny droplets of liquid water. The droplets form clouds.

**3** The clouds get heavy. Liquid water falls from them as rain.

**4** Rain falls on land and sea. The rain that falls on land flows into streams and rivers, and returns to the sea.

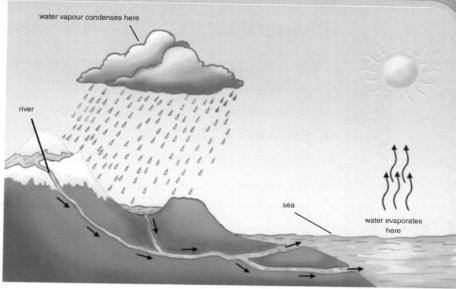

water vapour condenses here

river

sea

water evaporates here

## Keyword

**Water cycle** ➤ The journey water takes as it circulates from rivers, lakes and seas to the sky and back again

**Have a go!**

Place a few drops of water on two pieces of kitchen roll. Put one piece in a warm place and one in a cool place. Where does the water evaporate faster?

**Test yourself**

**1** Name the change of state from liquid to gas.

**2** Name the change of state from gas to liquid.

**3** The table gives the average temperature over one year for two cities.

| City | Average temperature (°C) |
|------|--------------------------|
| Moscow, Russia | 6 |
| Dar es Salaam, Tanzania | 26 |

Predict whether water will evaporate more quickly on a dry day in Moscow or on a dry day in Dar es Salaam.

**4** Explain why evaporation is important in the water cycle.

## Properties

There are millions of materials. Each material has its own properties.

Here are some examples of properties.

- **Hardness** – A hard material is difficult to scratch. A soft material is easy to scratch. Steel is harder than wood.

- **Transparency** – A transparent material lets light through. You can see through it. Glass is transparent. An **opaque** material does not allow light through. You cannot see through it. Wood is opaque.

- **Electrical** conductivity – Electricity travels easily through copper, so copper is an **electrical conductor**. Electricity cannot travel through wood, so wood is an **electrical insulator**.

- **Thermal conductivity** – Heat travels more easily through some materials than others. Heat travels easily through copper, so copper is a good **thermal conductor**. Heat does not travel easily through wood, so wood is a **thermal insulator**.

- **Response to magnets** – Magnets are attracted to iron and steel. Iron and steel are **magnetic**. Two other magnetic materials are nickel and cobalt.

## Using materials

The properties of different materials make them useful for different jobs.

**For example:**

- glass is transparent – it makes good windows

- copper is a good electrical conductor – it is used in wires.

Listen up 15

## Working scientifically

### Choosing an insulator

Ellie wants to find out if paper or fleece keeps soup warmer. She does a **fair test** to find out.

Cup A      Cup B

newspaper — soup

soup — fleece

The amount of soup in each cup is the same. The paper and fleece are the same thickness. Ellie uses a thermometer to check that both cups of soup start off at the same temperature.

After 10 minutes, Ellie uses a thermometer to measure the temperature of the soup in cup A and cup B. The soup in cup B is warmer than the soup in cup A. This shows that fleece is a better thermal insulator than paper.

**Top tip!** Thermal conductivity tells us about how well heat travels through a material. To help remember this, think about thermal underwear, which helps to stop heat leaving your body.

### Keywords

**Hardness** ➤ How easy it is to scratch a material. A hard material is difficult to scratch

**Transparency** ➤ A substance is transparent if it lets light through

**Conductivity** ➤ How easy it is for electricity or heat to travel through a material. The higher the value for electrical conductivity of a material, the more easily electricity travels through it

**Fair test** ➤ An investigation where you keep all the variables the same except the ones that you are changing and measuring

**Have a go!** Find an object in the kitchen. What material is it made from? How do the properties of the material make it suitable for its use? Repeat with two more objects.

**Test yourself**

❶ What is a transparent material?

❷ Write down four properties of wood.

❸ You can scratch steel with diamond. Which material is harder?

## Separating by sieving

mixture of sand and stones

sieve

sand

Imagine that a child drops many small stones into his sandpit. This makes a **mixture** of sand and stones. How can he get the stones out without missing any?

Mixing is a **reversible change**, so it is easy to get back the original materials. **Sieving** separates pieces of solid of different sizes.

## Dissolving and evaporating

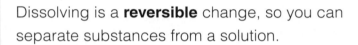

salt

Imagine adding salt to water, and stirring. Soon you cannot see the salt. However, the salt is still there. It is mixed up with the water. The salt has **dissolved** to make a **solution**.

Dissolving is a **reversible** change, so you can separate substances from a solution.

If you leave salt solution on a plate in a warm room, the water evaporates. The salt stays on the plate. The mixture has been separated by evaporation.

Day 1

salt solution

Five days later

salt

## Separating by filtering

Salt dissolves in water. It is **soluble**. However, some substances are not soluble. Sand never dissolves in water, no matter how much you stir it. Sand is not soluble.

filter paper

filter funnel

sand

water

You can use **sieving** or **filtering** to separate water from a substance that is not soluble (like sand).

## Working scientifically

### Soluble or not?

Sam wants to find out if some substances are soluble. He creates a table to record his data. He writes the **variable** he changes in the left-hand column (the substance), and the variable he observes (Does it dissolve?) in the other column.

| Substance | Does it dissolve? |
|-----------|-------------------|
| sugar | |
| flour | |
| cornflakes | |

## Keywords

**Mixture** ➤ A mixture is made up of two or more materials. It is often easy to separate the materials in a mixture

**Reversible change** ➤ A change in which you can get the original materials back. New substances are not made

**Dissolving** ➤ Mixing a solid with a liquid to make a solution

**Solution** ➤ A mixture of a solid with a liquid. You cannot see pieces of solid in a solution

**Soluble** ➤ A material is soluble if it dissolves in water

**Variable** ➤ Something you can change, measure or keep the same in an investigation

Listen up **16**

**Parent tip!**

Help your child to understand that dissolving, mixing and changes of state are reversible. This means that it is usually easy to get the starting materials back.

**Have a go!**

Add one spoonful of sugar to a glass of water. Does it dissolve? Repeat with two other substances. Are they soluble? Record your data in a table, like the one in the Working scientifically box.

**Test yourself**

1. What is a mixture?
2. Give examples of three types of reversible change.
3. Name a technique for separating sugar from sugar solution.
4. Filter paper has tiny holes. Use this information to suggest how filtration separates sand from water.

## Burning and rusting

Wood burns on a bonfire, forming ash, smoke and invisible gases. Burning is a change that is **not reversible**. Changes that are not reversible make new materials. You cannot get the starting materials back again.

This car is rusty. Its metal has joined with materials from the air to make a new material, rust. Rusting is not reversible.

## Useful changes

Most changes that happen in cooking are difficult to reverse. For example:

- you cannot get back the sugar, eggs, flour and butter when you bake a cake.

The materials we use every day were made from changes that are difficult to reverse. For example:

- wood comes from trees (which use carbon dioxide and water to grow)
- polythene is made in factories from a gas that comes from oil.

### Keyword

**Not reversible** ➤ A change that is not reversible makes new materials. It is difficult – or impossible – to get the starting materials back again

## Working scientifically

### Vinegar and bicarbonate of soda

Catherine and Sarah investigate a change that is difficult to reverse. They add a white powder, bicarbonate of soda, to vinegar. They see bubbles of a new material. The bubbling stops when the powder is used up.

The girls predict that the change will be quicker if the vinegar is warmer. They measure the time for the bubbling to stop at three different temperatures.

They make sure they do a fair test by **controlling** two **variables** – the amount of vinegar and the amount of powder.

Catherine and Sarah find out that their prediction is correct: the warmer the vinegar, the quicker the change.

### Keyword

**Control variables** ➤ The variables you keep the same in a fair test

**Parent tip!**

Discuss examples of changes that are reversible and those that are not usually reversible. For example, burning a match is not usually reversible but melting ice is reversible.

**Have a go!**

Do this activity with an adult.

➤ Light a candle and observe carefully. Identify one reversible change.

➤ Can you see any materials that were made in a change that is not reversible?

**Test yourself**

1. What is a control variable?
2. Underline the two reversible changes:
   - burning
   - melting
   - rusting
   - dissolving
3. Describe one difference between a reversible change and a change that is not reversible.
4. Is making toast a reversible change or a change that is not reversible? Explain your decision.

## Light sources

Some objects make light. These are light sources. Light sources include the Sun, other stars, lamps, torches, candles, computer screens and televisions.

You can see a light source when light travels from the source to your eye. Light travels in straight lines.

You must never look directly at the Sun. Its bright light can damage your eyes, even if you are wearing sunglasses.

## Reflecting light

Most objects are not light sources. Their surfaces **reflect** light.

This is how you see a ball outside:

1. Light from the Sun (a light source) travels in a straight line to the ball.
2. The surface of the ball reflects light.
3. Reflected light from the ball travels in a straight line to your eye.

Shiny surfaces reflect more light than dull surfaces. Light-coloured surfaces reflect more light than dark ones. You cannot see anything when there is no light, in a completely dark room.

Listen up
18

### Keywords

**Light source** ➤ An object that makes light

**Reflect** ➤ Light is reflected when it bounces off a surface

# Working scientifically

### Perfect periscope

Elliot is 150 cm tall. He wants to see over adults' heads in a crowd.
Elliot decides to make a periscope. The diagram shows how it works.

Elliot needs to know how tall to make his periscope. He collects data by measuring the heights of five adults. He calculates their average height, which is 168 cm. He also writes down the height of the tallest person, which is 190 cm. Elliot uses this data, and his own height, to work out the best height for his periscope.

**Top tip!**

The Moon is not a light source. You can see it because it reflects light from the Sun.

**Have a go!**

Make a list of all the light sources you can find around your home.

**Test yourself**

1. Name five light sources.
2. Which reflects more candlelight – a mirror or a piece of black paper of the same size?
3. Draw a diagram to explain how you see a cuddly toy when you shine a torch at it.
4. Look again at the Working scientifically box. Use the data to calculate the best height for Elliot's periscope. Show how you worked out your answer.

## Transparent or opaque? ✓

Light travels through transparent materials. That is why you can see through glass, or parts of this butterfly's wing.

Light does not travel through **opaque** materials, so you cannot see through them. Wood is opaque.

## Making shadows

A **shadow** forms when an opaque object blocks light from a light source.

In this diagram, light travels from the street light in straight lines. Some light hits the cat. This light travels no further. There is an area of darkness, or shadow, behind the cat.

Some light from the street light travels past the cat. This is why there is light around the shadow.

## Lengthening shadows

**Short shadow**   **Long shadow**

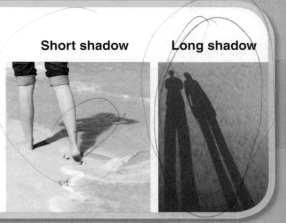

The size of a shadow depends on the position of the light source.

At midday the Sun is above you in the sky. Your shadow is short. In the evening the Sun is low in the sky. Your shadow is longer.

### Keywords

**Opaque** ➤ Light cannot travel through an opaque object

**Shadow** ➤ An area of darkness on a surface caused by an opaque object blocking out light

# Working scientifically

## Shadow size

Joshua asks a scientific question:

> How does the angle of a light source affect the length of a shadow?

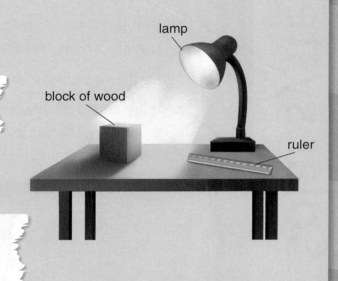

Joshua plans an investigation to answer his question. He decides which variables to change, measure and control:

- variable to change – angle of light source
- variable to measure – length of shadow
- variables to control – size and shape of object

Joshua collects some data. He finds out that the smaller the angle of the light source above the table, the longer the shadow.

**Parent tip!** Find an object, such as a mug. Shine a light at it from different angles. Can you make the shape of the shadow change?

**Have a go!** Take a torch into a dark room. Use your hand and the torch to make shadows on the wall. Can you make them bigger and smaller?

**Test yourself**

1. What is a shadow?
2. What is the difference between a transparent object and an opaque object?
3. Look again at the Working scientifically box. Name one piece of equipment that Joshua needs for his investigation.
4. Constance has a shadow puppet. How can she make the shadow bigger?

## The solar system

The **Sun** is the star at the centre of our **solar system**. It is a light source and gives out heat. It is spherical.

The Earth is a **planet** that orbits the Sun. Its shape is roughly spherical.

There are seven other planets in our solar system: Mercury, Venus, Mars, Jupiter, Saturn, Uranus and Neptune. All the planets **orbit** the Sun. Their orbits are roughly circular.

## The Moon

A **moon** is a natural object that orbits a planet. Jupiter has four big moons and many more small ones.

The Earth has one moon. It is roughly spherical. The Moon takes 27 days to orbit Earth.

## Working scientifically

### Ideas about the solar system

Ptolemy was a scientist. He lived in Egypt, two thousand years ago. Ptolemy used observations from other scientists, and his own ideas, to develop a theory. The Earth is at the centre of the Universe, he said. The Sun, and other planets, orbit Earth.

One thousand years later, an Arab scientist, Alhazen, noticed some problems with Ptolemy's ideas. He wrote a book to explain these problems.

Copernicus (1473–1543)

Copernicus lived in Poland five hundred years ago. He also criticised Ptolemy's theory. He thought it unlikely that thousands of stars could orbit Earth every 24 hours. It is more likely that Earth is rotating, he said. Copernicus developed a new theory, that the Earth and other planets orbit the Sun.

**Parent tip!**

The section above on ideas about our solar system shows how scientific theories can change over time as new evidence is obtained.

### Keywords

**Sun** ➤ The star at the centre of our solar system

**Solar system** ➤ The Sun, and the planets and other objects that orbit it

**Planet** ➤ A big object that orbits a star

**Orbit** ➤ The circular (or elliptical) path an object in space takes around another object in space

**Moon** ➤ A natural object that orbits a planet

**Have a go!**

Use the Internet to find out as much as you can about a planet of your choice. Make a poster to display your findings.

**Test yourself**

1. What object does the Earth orbit?

2. What object does the Moon orbit?

3. Describe one way in which the Sun, Earth and Moon are similar.

4. Describe one difference between the Earth and the Moon.

## Day and night

The Earth is rotating on its **axis**. The Earth takes 24 hours to rotate once.

The rotating Earth gives us day and night. At any one time, half the Earth faces the Sun. This part of the Earth is light, so it is daytime here. The other half of the Earth faces away from the Sun. This part of the Earth is in darkness. It is night-time here.

## From east to west

The Sun **appears to move** across the sky, from east to west. In fact, it is the Earth that is moving; the Sun is stationary.

The Earth rotates towards the east. This explains why we see the Sun rise in the east in the morning. As the Earth continues to spin, the Sun appears to move across the sky. In the evening the Sun sets in the west.

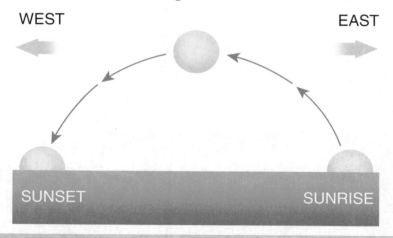

Listen up 21

### Keyword

**Axis** ➤ An imaginary line between the North Pole and the South Pole, going through the centre of the Earth

## Working scientifically

### Time of day

One day after school, Jemima looks at her globe. She notices that Peru and Singapore are on opposite sides of the Earth.

Peru

She makes a prediction:

When it is daytime in Peru, it is night-time in Singapore.

Jemima uses the Internet to find out the times in the two places.

| Place | Time |
| --- | --- |
| Peru | 11:00 (morning) |
| Singapore | 23:00 (night) |

The data show that her prediction is correct.

**Top tip!** Don't confuse the scientific meaning of the word **day** (the time for the Earth to rotate once on its axis) with the usual meaning of the word **day** (daytime, the part of the day when it is light).

**Have a go!** Use a ball and a torch to model the Earth rotating on its axis. Can you use your model to explain why we have day and night?

**Test yourself**

1. How long does the Earth take to rotate on its axis?
2. In which direction does the Earth rotate – towards the east or west?
3. Explain why it is sometimes dark and sometimes light.
4. Explain why the Sun seems to move across the sky.

## What can forces do?

**Forces** can be pushes or pulls. They can make things move, and make them move faster. They can slow things down and make them stop.

Forces also change the direction of moving objects. They change shapes too, by squashing and stretching.

## Friction

**Friction** is a force that acts against things that are moving.

For example, to make a bike start moving, you must overcome the friction between the tyre and the road. When you pull on the brakes, the force of friction between the brake blocks and the tyres makes the bike stop.

## Air resistance and water resistance

Air resistance and water resistance make things slow down.

When you swim, you experience **water resistance**.

Flying birds and falling parachutes experience **air resistance**.

Listen up
22

### Keywords

**Forces** ➤ Forces can change the movement and shapes of objects

**Friction** ➤ A force that acts between surfaces and slows down or stops things that are moving

**Water resistance** ➤ A force that slows things down in water

**Air resistance** ➤ A force that slows things down in air

# Working scientifically

## Surfaces and friction

Callum asks a scientific question:

> Is there more friction between rough surfaces or smooth ones?

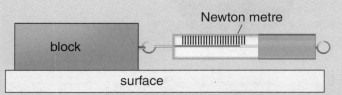

block

Newton metre

surface

He measures the force to pull a smooth wooden block over a smooth wooden surface. Then he measures the force to pull a sandpaper-covered block over a sandpaper-covered surface. He wants to make sure his results are accurate, so he repeats each reading three times and calculates an average value. He measures the size of his force in Newtons (N).

| Surfaces | Force to pull block (N) | | | |
|---|---|---|---|---|
| | first time | second time | third time | average |
| rough sandpaper | 11 | 10 | 9 | 10 |
| smooth wood | 5 | 7 | 6 | |

Callum writes a conclusion:

> The smoother the surfaces, the smaller the frictional force.

**Have a go!**

Make a parachute from string and a piece of plastic cut from an old bag. Can you make another parachute that falls more slowly?

**Test yourself**

1. What is friction?
2. Name three forces that act between moving surfaces.
3. Look again at the Working scientifically box. Calculate the average force to pull the block across the wood in Callum's experiment. Show how you worked out your answer.
4. Keira makes two parachutes to carry a model person. She drops them from the same height at the same time. Parachute A reaches the floor before parachute B. Which parachute experiences more air resistance?

## Gravity

If you drop a ball, the Earth pulls it down. The force of **gravity** acts between the Earth and the ball.

The Earth pulls the ball down even though it is not touching the ball. Gravity is a **non-contact force**.

## Magnets

In this picture, a **magnetic force** is pulling the magnets together. The magnets attract each other. The North Pole of one magnet is facing the South Pole of the other magnet.

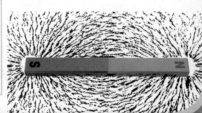

If you turn one of the magnets round, they **repel** each other. Two magnets push away from each other when:

- their North Poles face each other
- their South Poles face each other.

Magnetic forces are **non-contact forces**. They can act even when they are not touching.

Magnets attract **magnetic materials**. They do not attract non-magnetic materials.

| Magnetic materials | Non-magnetic materials |
|---|---|
| iron | aluminium |
| steel | copper |
| nickel | gold |
| cobalt | all materials that are not metals |

Listen up
23

## Working scientifically

### Comparing magnets

Catherine has two magnets. She wants to see which one is stronger. She counts the number of paper clips that hang in a chain from each magnet.

Catherine uses her results to make a prediction:

Magnet B will hold more nails than magnet A.

## Keywords

**Gravity** ➤ The force between two objects. It pulls things towards the Earth

**Magnetic force** ➤ The force between two magnets, or between a magnet and a magnetic material

**Repel** ➤ Push away

**Magnetic material** ➤ A material that is attracted to a magnet

**Parent tip!**

Check that your child knows that gravity and magnetic forces are non-contact forces. They can act between objects that are not touching.

**Have a go!**

Walk around your home. Make a list of all the things you can find that include magnets.

**Test yourself**

1. What is gravity?
2. Underline the materials that are magnetic:

   copper    iron    wood

   steel        leather
3. Nathan holds two magnets close together, with their North Poles facing each other. Predict what will happen.
4. Look again at the Working scientifically box. Suggest how Catherine could find out if her prediction was correct.

## Pulleys

A **pulley** is a **simple machine**. It makes lifting easier.

For example, pulleys are used by builders to help them lift heavy loads.

The pulley opposite has two wheels. Two sections of rope support the load. The force to lift the load with the pulley is half the force needed to lift the load without the pulley.

50 kg lifting force

100 kg load

## Levers

A lever is a **simple machine**. It makes a small force have a big effect.

In this picture, a decorator uses a screwdriver to open the lid of a paint tin. The screwdriver is a **lever**. It applies a bigger force to the lid than you could apply with your hand.

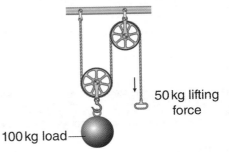

### Keywords

**Pulley** ➤ A system of wheels and ropes that make it easier to lift things

**Simple machine** ➤ A device that changes the direction or size of a force

**Lever** ➤ A straight rod with a pivot. You can use it to exert a big force over a small distance at one end by exerting a smaller force over a bigger distance at the other end

Listen up
24

### Investigating levers

Lim asks a scientific question:

> Is it easier to open a tin of paint with a short screwdriver or a long screwdriver?

Lim does an experiment to answer his question. The evidence shows that he needs to apply less force with a longer lever.

# Gears

The **gear system** on a bike is a **simple machine**. You can choose a bigger or smaller cog on the back wheel to change gears.

Back cogs are usually smaller than front cogs. Back cogs turn faster than front cogs. The turning force of the back cog is smaller.

A bigger back cog turns more slowly than a smaller back cog. The turning force of a bigger cog is bigger than the turning force of a smaller cog. The bigger cog is better for going uphill.

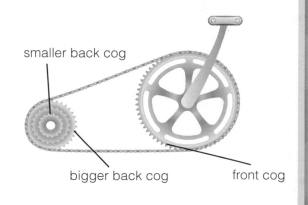

smaller back cog

bigger back cog          front cog

## Keyword

**Gear system** ➤ A system of cogs that allows a small turning force to have a greater effect

**Top tip!** Levers, gear systems and pulleys are all simple machines.

**Have a go!** Try out Lim's investigation above. Ask an adult to help. Do you agree with his findings?

**Test yourself**

1. What is a simple machine?
2. Give examples of three types of simple machine.
3. Predict whether it is easier to open a paint tin using a coin or a screwdriver. Explain your prediction.

## Making sounds

Sounds are made by **vibrating** objects.

**For example:**

- when you bang a drum, its skin vibrates
- when you play a ukulele, its strings vibrate.

Vibrating skins and strings make the air vibrate. The vibrations travel through the air. If the air vibrations enter your ear, you hear them as sounds.

Sound cannot travel through a vacuum, which is just empty space. It needs a **medium** to travel through, such as air, a liquid (such as water) or a solid (such as wood). You cannot hear sound in space.

## Volume

Big, strong vibrations make loud sounds. For example, if you bang a drum hard, the vibrations are big and the drum makes a loud sound.

Small, weak vibrations make quiet sounds. For example, if you bang a drum gently, the vibrations are small and the drum makes a quiet sound.

The loudness of a sound is also called its **volume**. Turning up the volume makes a louder sound.

Next to a vibrating fire bell, the sound is very loud. As you move away from the sound source, the sound gets fainter.

## Pitch

The **pitch** of a sound is how high or low it is. Pitch is nothing to do with loudness. A high-pitched sound can be loud or quiet. A low-pitched sound can be loud or quiet.

## Working scientifically

### Investigating pitch

Clarice has a scientific question:

> How does the thickness of a guitar string affect the pitch of the sound?

Clarice plucks guitar strings of different thicknesses. She spots a pattern. The thicker the string, the lower the pitch.

Clarice investigates some more questions. She finds out that:

- the longer the string, the lower the pitch
- the tighter the string, the higher the pitch.

### Keywords

**Vibrating** ➤ An object is vibrating if it is moving backwards and forwards again and again

**Medium** ➤ A material that sound travels through. A medium can be in the solid, liquid or gas state

**Volume** ➤ The loudness or quietness of a sound

**Pitch** ➤ How high or low a sound is

**Parent tip!**

The investigation in **Have a go!** below demonstrates very clearly that sounds are made when an object (the speaker) vibrates.

**Have a go!**

With an adult, position a speaker so that its vibrations are vertical. Play some music, loudly. Place a few grains of *uncooked* rice on the speaker. Watch what happens.

**Test yourself**

1. What must an object be doing in order to make a sound?
2. Give examples of three materials that sound can travel through.
3. What do you hear as you get further from a sound source?
4. Predict which instrument makes sounds of lower pitch – a violin or a viola. Why? Use the pictures to help you.

violin          viola

## Using electricity

How many electrical devices have you used today? Can you imagine life without mobile phones, computers and fridges?

## Electrical circuits

In an electrical device, the electricity flows around a loop called a **circuit**. Electricity only flows if the circuit is complete. It must not have any gaps.

A simple circuit may include:

- a **cell** to push electricity around the circuit
- components such as bulbs, buzzers or motors
- wires to connect the cells and components
- a switch.

**motor**                **cell**                **bulb**

**Note:** people usually call a cell a battery. However, scientists say that a battery is two or more cells.

## Symbols

You can use symbols to represent the components in a circuit.

| Component | Symbol |
|-----------|--------|
| cell | —│┝— |
| bulb | —⊗— |
| buzzer | ⏚ |
| motor | (M) |
| wire | —— |
| switch | —o o— |

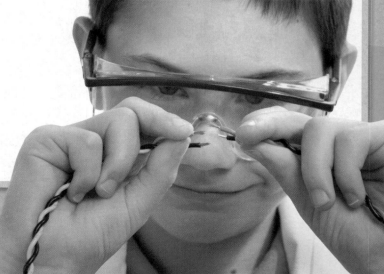

Listen up 26

## Working scientifically

### Conductors and insulators

Mo makes an electrical circuit with a gap. He wants to know which materials he can use to connect across the gap.

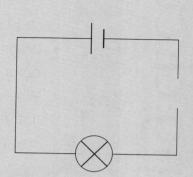

Mo tests different materials. The bulb lights when he connects copper or aluminium foil across the gap. It does not light when he connects wood or paper across the gap.

Mo uses his evidence to write a conclusion:

> Electricity flows through copper and aluminium.
> It does not flow through wood or paper.

Metals are good **conductors** of electricity. Most other materials are **electrical insulators**.

## Keywords

**Circuit** ➤ Electricity flows around a complete circuit

**Cell** ➤ A cell pushes electricity around a complete circuit

**Conductor** ➤ A substance that electricity can flow through

**Electrical insulator** ➤ A substance that electricity cannot flow through

**Top tip!** If you make a circuit and it doesn't work, check that there are no gaps in it. If it still doesn't work, test each component, one at a time, in another circuit that you know does work.

**Have a go!** List all the electrical devices you can find at home.

**Test yourself**

1. Draw the circuit symbol for a bulb.
2. What happens if there is a gap in an electrical circuit?
3. List two electrical conductors and two electrical insulators.
4. Name the part of a mobile phone that pushes electricity around its circuits.

## Switches

A **switch** turns a device on or off.

Look at this circuit.

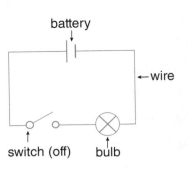

- When the switch is closed (on), the circuit is complete. Electricity flows. The bulb lights.
- When the switch is open (off), there is a gap in the circuit. Electricity cannot flow. The bulb does not light.

## Brightness and loudness

In a circuit, the number of cells affects bulb brightness and buzzer loudness.

The cell **voltage** also makes a difference. The higher the voltage, the greater the 'push' that makes the electricity flow.

Circuits A and B below are almost identical, but circuit B has an extra cell. The bulb in circuit B is brighter.

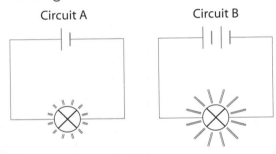

The cell in circuit D below has a higher voltage than the cell in circuit C. The buzzer in circuit D makes a louder sound.

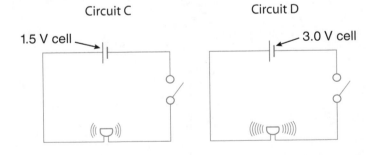

## Keywords

**Switch** ➤ A component that turns a device on and off

**Voltage** ➤ The 'push' that makes electricity flow around a circuit

## Circuit investigation

Sophie investigates how the number of cells affects the loudness of a buzzer. She sets up this circuit.

She designs a table for her results. She writes the variable she changes in the left-hand column, and the variable she observes in the right-hand column.

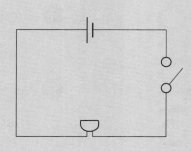

| Number of cells | Buzzer loudness |
|---|---|
| 1 | quiet |
| 2 | medium |
| 3 | loud |

**Top tip!** If your circuit is not working, check the switch. Is it closed?

---

**Have a go!** Use the Internet to find out about electrical safety. Search for 'electrical safety KS2'. Tell an adult what you have found out.

**Test yourself**

1 What is a switch?

2 Look at the Working scientifically box. Which variable does Sophie change in her investigation?

3 Look at the Working scientifically box. Write a conclusion for Sophie's investigation.

4 Give three reasons to explain why the bulb does not light in the circuit below.

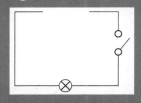

# Classifying living things

**❶** Circle **four** invertebrates. **(4 marks)**

> snake    shark    bee    spider    ant    frog    snail    bat

**❷** Fill in the gaps with the correct words. **(3 marks)**

There are two big groups of plants: non-flowering plants and

............................ plants. Non-flowering plants include mosses and

............................. Grasses are in the ............................ plants group.

**❸** Write down **two** things that all birds have in common. **(2 marks)**

...................................................................................................................

...................................................................................................................

**❹** There are about 60 000 different types of vertebrate. The chart shows
the percentage of this number that are in each vertebrate group.

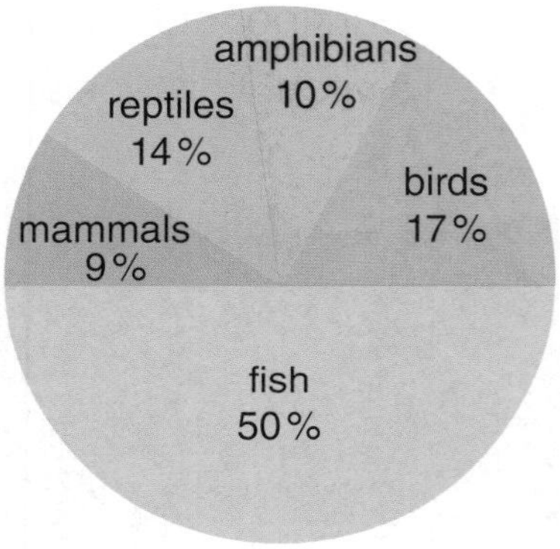

**a.** Which group has the biggest
number of different types?

............................

**(1 mark)**

**b.** Which group has the smallest
number of different types?

............................

**(1 mark)**

amphibians
10 %

reptiles
14 %

birds
17 %

mammals
9 %

fish
50 %

**❺** Use the key to find out which tree
the leaf is from. Then circle the answer.

**(1 mark)**

**pine    horse chestnut    juniper    beech**

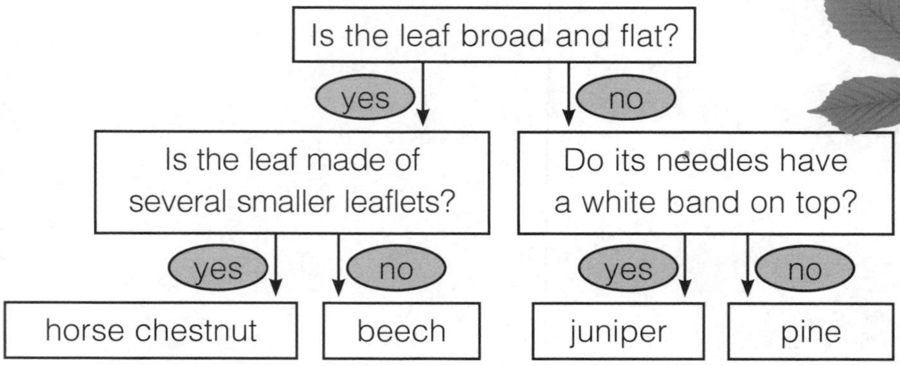

Is the leaf broad and flat?

yes → no →

Is the leaf made of
several smaller leaflets?

Do its needles have
a white band on top?

yes → no →          yes → no →

horse chestnut    beech    juniper    pine

Total $\frac{}{12}$

## Plants

**1** Fill in the gap with the correct word. **(1 mark)**

Plants need these things to grow: air, nutrients, light,

space and ..............................

**2** Fill in the missing labels. **(2 marks)**

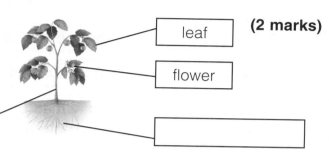

leaf

flower

**3** What is the job of leaves? Tick the box next to the correct answer.

**(1 mark)**

**a.** support the plant ☐ **b.** make seeds ☐

**c.** take in nutrients ☐ **d.** make food ☐

**4** Ollie adds different-coloured food dyes to jars of water. He puts a white flower in each jar. The next day he looks at his flowers. This is what he sees.

blue food dye
and water

red food dye
and water

yellow food dye
and water

**a.** Fill in the missing observation. **(1 mark)**

| Colour of food dye | Observation |
|---|---|
| blue | flowers are ............................. |
| red | flowers are red |
| yellow | flowers are yellow |

**b.** Which variable did Ollie change? ............................. **(1 mark)**

**c.** Explain why the flowers change colour. **(2 marks)**

..................................................................................................

..................................................................................................

**Top tip!** When there are two marks for a question, write about two things in your answer.

Total —— 8

# Life cycles

**1** Draw lines to match each stage of the human life cycle with something that happens in that stage. **(4 marks)**

**Stage**

child

baby

adult

teenager

**What happens**

they are fully grown

their body changes rapidly

they learn to walk and talk

they feed on milk from their mother's breasts

**2** Tick the boxes next to the **two** animals that metamorphose. **(2 marks)**

bee ☐     ladybird ☐

horse ☐     whale ☐

**3** Write these words in the correct order for the life cycle of a butterfly, starting from the beginning of the life cycle. **(4 marks)**

**pupa        egg        adult        larva**

.............................., .............................., .............................., ..............................

**4** The picture shows the stages in the life cycle of a frog. Write the missing labels in the boxes. **(4 marks)**

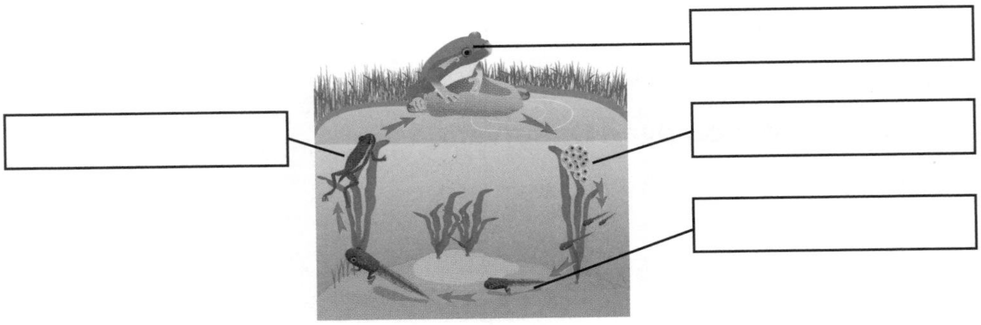

**5** Describe the life cycle of a chicken, starting with the egg. **(4 marks)**

.................................................................................................

.................................................................................................

.................................................................................................

Total —— 18

# Reproduction

**1** The text shows the stages in the sexual reproduction of a flowering plant.

**Stage**

| pollination |

| fertilisation |

| dispersal |

**What happens**

| pollen joins with ovules to make seeds |

| seeds move away from the plant |

| pollen travels from the stamen of one flower to the stigma of another |

**a.** Draw lines to match each stage with what happens in that stage. **(3 marks)**

**b.** Which **two** stages can animals help with? **(2 marks)**

...................................................    ...................................................

**2** The table shows the time from fertilisation to birth for five mammals.

| Mammal | Time from fertilisation to birth (days) |
|--------|------------------------------------------|
| cat | 65 |
| dog | 60 |
| mouse | 20 |
| rat | 20 |
| squirrel | 35 |

Do not forget to label the *x* and *y* axis of your chart.

**a.** On a separate piece of paper, draw a bar chart showing the data in the table. Write the mammal names on the *x* axis and the time from fertilisation to birth on the *y* axis. **(5 marks)**

**b.** This table gives some more data.

| Mammal | Time from fertilisation to birth (days) | How heavy is the adult mammal (kg)? |
|--------|------------------------------------------|--------------------------------------|
| cat | 65 | 5 |
| human | 275 | 70 |
| horse | 335 | 500 |
| sperm whale | 535 | 55 000 |

Use the data in the table to complete the sentence below. **(1 mark)**

As the time from fertilisation to birth increases, ..........................................

.......................................................................................... .

Total $\dfrac{}{11}$

## Heart and blood

**❶** Look at the diagram. Write the letter of the label that points to the heart. ............ **(1 mark)**

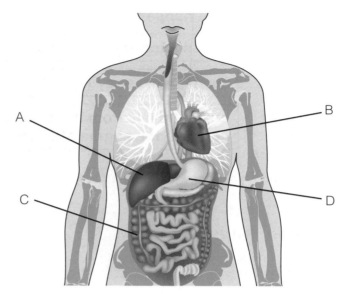

**❷** Circle **three** things that blood carries around your body. **(3 marks)**

oxygen    nutrients    water    urine    saliva

**❸** Katie measures the pulse rate of four friends. She measures the pulse of each friend three times.

| Name | Pulse rate (beats per minute) | | | |
|---|---|---|---|---|
| | first time | second time | third time | average |
| Saniyah | 80 | 85 | 75 | |
| Rachel | 180 | 170 | 160 | 170 |
| Wilbur | 69 | 79 | 74 | 74 |
| Kieran | 75 | 81 | 78 | 75 |

**a.** Calculate Saniyah's average pulse rate. **(2 marks)**

..............................................................................................................

..............................................................................................................

**b.** Who has been running? Give a reason for your choice. **(2 marks)**

Name: ................................

Reason: ...........................................................................................

Total ⎯ 8

# Skeletons and muscles

**1** What is your skeleton made of? ................................ **(1 mark)**

**2** List the **three** jobs of the skeleton. **(3 marks)**

.................................   ................................   ................................

**3** Here is a picture of an elephant skeleton.

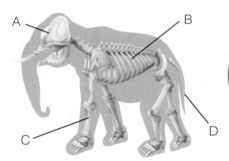

Make sure your child realises that mammal skeletons have many similarities. Ribs always protect organs such as the heart. The skull always protects the brain.

Parent tip!

**a.** Write the letter which points to the ribs. ................................ **(1 mark)**

**b.** Write the letter which points to the skull. ................................ **(1 mark)**

**c.** What is the job of the skull? **(1 mark)**

..................................................................................................

**4** Look at the two skeletons.

wolf

giraffe

**a.** List **two** similarities between the two skeletons. **(2 marks)**

..................................................................................................

..................................................................................................

**b.** List **two** differences between the two skeletons. **(2 marks)**

..................................................................................................

..................................................................................................

Total —— 11

## Healthy living

**❶** Draw lines to match each food to its main nutrient. **(4 marks)**

**Food**

| pasta |
| chicken |
| butter |
| fruit |

**Nutrient**

| fat |
| carbohydrate |
| vitamins and minerals |
| protein |

**Parent tip!**

When you are eating with your child, discuss the main nutrients in different foods.

**❷** Circle the correct **bold** word in each pair. **(5 marks)**

The two nutrients whose main job is to provide you with energy are **carbohydrates/proteins** and **vitamins/fats**. The nutrients whose main job is to keep everything working properly are **vitamins/fat** and **carbohydrates/minerals**. The main nutrient that your body uses to repair damage is **protein/fat**.

**❸** What is a drug?
Tick the **best** answer. **(1 mark)**

A substance that affects how your body works. ☐

A substance that harms your body. ☐

A substance that makes you behave strangely. ☐

A substance that makes you better if you are ill. ☐

**❹** Alcohol is a drug. What effects can it have on a person?
Tick the **three** correct answers. **(3 marks)**

It can damage their heart. ☐

It might make them sick. ☐

It can damage their brain. ☐

It makes them drive more safely. ☐

Total ___ 13

# Digestion

**1** Fill in the missing labels using the correct words.　　　**(7 marks)**

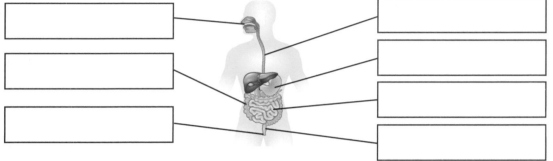

large intestine　　stomach　　small intestine
oesophagus　　mouth　　anus　　rectum

**2** What happens in each of these parts of the digestive system?　**(3 marks)**

　**a.** Mouth

　.......................................................................................................

　**b.** Stomach

　.......................................................................................................

　**c.** Anus

　.......................................................................................................

**3** Draw lines to match each type of tooth to its job.　　　**(3 marks)**

**Type of tooth**　　　　　　**Job**

| incisors |
| canines |
| molars |

| tear food such as meat |
| grind and chew food |
| bite off pieces of food |

**4** Look at the skull in the picture. Do you think the animal ate mainly meat or mainly plants? Give a reason for your decision.　**(2 marks)**

Answer: ...................................

Reason: ...........................................................................

　.................................................................................

　.................................................................................

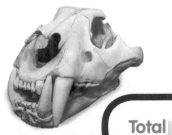

Total $\frac{}{15}$

## Food chains

**1** Look at this food chain.

grass    →    wildebeest    →    lion

**a.** What do the arrows mean? **(1 mark)**

.................................................................................................................

**b.** Name the predator in the food chain. **(1 mark)**

.................................................................................................................

**c.** Name the producer in the food chain. **(1 mark)**

.................................................................................................................

**d.** Name the prey in the food chain. **(1 mark)**

.................................................................................................................

**2** Here is a seaside food chain.

seaweed  →  limpet  →  crab  →  seagull

**a.** Which animal in the food chain is both predator and prey? **(1 mark)**

.................................................................................................................

**b.** Predict **two** things that might happen if people take lots of crabs from the beach. **(2 marks)**

.................................................................................................................

.................................................................................................................

.................................................................................................................

Remember, **producers** make their own food. **Prey** are animals eaten by other animals. **Predators** eat other animals.

Top tip!

Total —— 7

# Changing environments

**1** Edward digs a pond in his garden.
Here is a food chain showing some of the living things in and around the pond.

pond weed ➝ water boatman ➝ newt ➝ fox

**a.** Name the producer in the food chain. .................................. **(1 mark)**

**b.** Predict what might happen to the number of water boatmen in the pond if Edward removes the pond weed. **(1 mark)**

.......................................................................................................

**c.** Edward buys a fox scarer for his garden. It makes a high-pitched sound that foxes do not like. The foxes move away from Edward's garden.

Predict what might happen to the number of newts in the pond.

.................................................................................... **(1 mark)**

Explain your answer. **(1 mark)**

.......................................................................................................

.......................................................................................................

**d.** When the foxes go away, hedgehogs start eating the newts.
Draw a new food chain showing the pond weed, water boatman, newt and hedgehog. **(1 mark)**

**Parent tip!**

There are many possible answers to questions like these, because the animals in these food chains are also in other food chains. One food chain cannot give the complete picture.

Total ——
5

# Evolution

**❶** Read the information about elephants. Then complete
the table. **(4 marks)**

Adult elephants are huge, so other animals do not attack
them. They use their trunks to reach food high up in trees,
as well as to get food and water from the ground.

Their tusks are also useful. They use them to strip bark
from trees, which they then eat. They also use them to
dig to find water under dried-up rivers.

They flap their enormous ears to cool the blood in them.
The cooler blood then travels around their bodies.

| Adaptation | How the adaptation helps them to survive |
|---|---|
| big size | ................................................................ |
| trunks | ................................................................ |
| tusks | ................................................................ |
| big ears | ................................................................ |

**❷** The steps below describe how head lice evolve, but they are in the
wrong order.

Write numbers next to each step to show the correct order. The first
one has been done for you. **(4 marks)**

**A** Individual head lice are not the same. They show variation. `1`

**B** The surviving head lice lay eggs. The eggs hatch. ☐

**C** Some head lice have features which stop head lice shampoo
killing them. These head lice survive. The others die. ☐

**D** The steps are repeated. Eventually, all head lice have the
features that stop head lice shampoo killing them. ☐

**E** The offspring from the eggs are likely to have the features
that stop head lice shampoo killing them. ☐

Total — 8

# Rocks and soil

**1** Hilary has three rocks. She tries scratching them with different objects. The table shows her results.

| Rock | Can I scratch it with my fingernail? | Can I scratch it with a knife? |
|------|--------------------------------------|--------------------------------|
| A | yes | yes |
| B | no | yes |
| C | no | no |

**a.** Which rock is easiest to scratch? ............................ **(1 mark)**

**b.** Which rock might be granite? ............................ **(1 mark)**

**2** Riley has three different rocks, each of a different type. He weighs his rocks. Then he puts them in water. A week later he weighs the rocks again. His results are in the table.

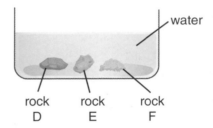

| Rock | Mass of rock at start (g) | Mass of rock at end (g) | Mass of water that soaked into the rock (g) |
|------|---------------------------|-------------------------|---------------------------------------------|
| D | 50 | 59 | 9 |
| E | 50 | 50 | 0 |
| F | 50 | 67 | |

**a.** How much water soaked into rock F? Show your working. **(2 marks)**

.................................................................................................................

.................................................................................................................

**b.** Which rock is not porous? ............................ **(1 mark)**

**c.** Which rock is probably made up of crystals? ............................ **(1 mark)**

When you do a calculation, show how you work out the answer.

Top tip!

Total —— 6

# Solid, liquid or gas?

**1** Fill in the gap with the correct word. **(1 mark)**

The three states of matter are solid, ...*Liquid*... and gas.

**2** What is the name of solid water?
Tick the box next to the correct answer. **(1 mark)**

ice ☑               water vapour ☐

steam ☐             condensation ☐

**3** Fill in the table. **(4 marks)**

| State | Can you squash it? | Does it flow? |
|---|---|---|
| gas | *Yes* | yes |
| liquid | *No* | *Yes* |
| *Solid* | no | no |

**4** Seth has some water. He puts it in the freezer and it becomes solid. What change of state happens in the freezer? **(1 mark)**

*It freezes* ○ ○ ○ ○ ○ ➡ ⬡⬡⬡

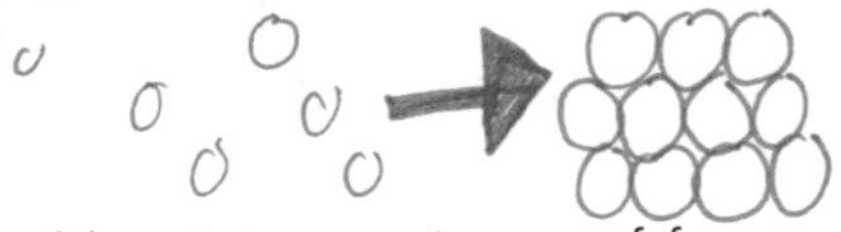

**5** The table shows the melting temperatures of four materials.

| Material | Melting temperature (°C) |
|---|---|
| copper | 1083 |
| gold | 1063 |
| iron | 1535 |
| silver | 961 |

**a.** Which material in the table melts at the highest temperature?

...*Iron*... **(1 mark)**

**b.** What is the difference between the melting points of copper and gold? Show your working. **(2 marks)**

...*20 °C*...

Total —— 10

# Water cycle

**1** The diagram shows the water cycle. Fill in the gaps in the boxes.

**(2 marks)**

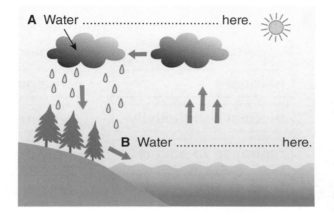

A Water ........................... here.

B Water ........................... here.

**2** Circle the correct **bold** word in each pair. **(5 marks)**

The Sun **heats/cools** water in the sea. Some water **evaporates/condenses** to make water vapour. This rises and **heats/cools**. It **evaporates/condenses** to make liquid water in clouds. Liquid water falls from clouds as **rain/snow**.

**3** Felix does an experiment to find out where water evaporates quickest. He puts some water on three different pieces of kitchen roll. He puts the pieces of kitchen roll in different places and leaves them for two hours.

**a.** What does Felix change in his investigation?

.......... kitchen roll ................................................ **(1 mark)**

**b.** How could Felix make his experiment fair?

.......... By NOT changing the kitchen roll. the same H₂O **(1 mark)**

**c.** Draw lines to match each place to the most likely observation after two hours.

**(3 marks)**

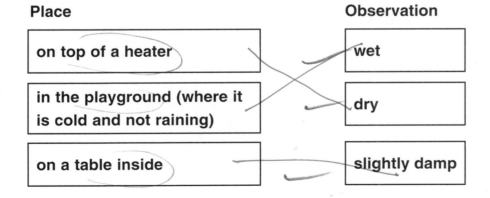

| Place | Observation |
|---|---|
| **on top of a heater** | wet |
| **in the playground (where it is cold and not raining)** | dry |
| **on a table inside** | slightly damp |

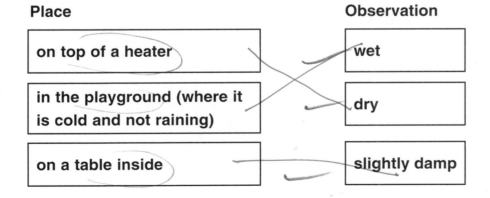

Total — 12

States of Matter

# Using materials

**❶** Draw lines to match each property to its meaning. **(4 marks)**

**Property**

| hardness |
| thermal conductivity |
| response to magnets |
| transparency |

**Meaning**

| whether it is attracted to a magnet |
| whether it is see-through |
| how well heat travels through it |
| how easy or difficult it is to scratch |

**❷** Which properties of copper make it suitable for electric cables? Tick the boxes next to the **two** correct answers. **(2 marks)**

It is a good thermal conductor. ☐

It is shiny. ☐

It is a good electrical conductor. ✓

It is bendy. ✓

**❸** Circle the **two** materials that are magnetic. **(2 marks)**

(iron)    **wood**    **gold**    (steel)

**❹** The table shows the hardness of some materials: the higher the number, the harder the material.

Draw a bar chart from the data in the table. **(4 marks)**

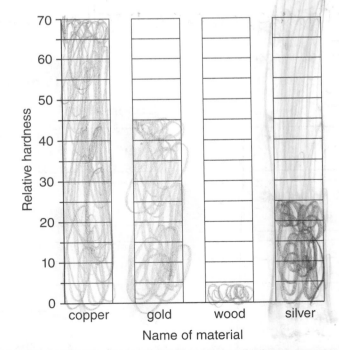

| Material | Relative hardness |
|---|---|
| copper | 70 |
| gold | 45 |
| wood | 5 |
| silver | 25 |

Relative hardness / Name of material

Total 12

## Mixtures

**1** Four children put some blue crystals in a glass.

They add water and stir. After stirring, there are no crystals. The picture shows what they see.

Top tip!

It is easy to get **melting** and **dissolving** muddled up. Make sure you know the difference.

The children discuss their observations:

**Max**
The blue crystals have melted.

**Roisin**
The blue crystals have condensed.

**Sunila**
The blue crystals have evaporated.

**Kassim**
The blue crystals have dissolved.

Which child is correct? Write their name here. ......Kassim...... **(1 mark)**

**2** Marcus has a mixture of flour and sand.

Describe in detail how he could separate the mixture. **(4 marks)**

He could seperate the mixture by
filtering it ① pour boiling water over a
container with filter paper and the sand and flour rush.

**3** Fill in the gaps with the correct words. **(6 marks)**

| solution | dissolves | soluble | filtering | dissolve |

Harriet adds salt to water and stirs. The salt ...dissolves... to

make a ...solution... This shows that salt is ...soluble...

in water.

Then she gets another cup of water. She adds sand to the water.

The sand does not ...dissolve... in water. It is not ...soluble...

You can separate sand and water by ...filtering...

Total 11

## New materials

**①** Write **T** next to the statements that are true and **F** next to the statements that are false. **(4 marks)**

**A** If a change is not reversible, it is easy to get the starting materials back again. [ F ]

**B** If a change is reversible, it is difficult to get the starting materials back again. [ F ]

**C** If a change is reversible, it is easy to get the starting materials back again. [ T ]

**D** If a change is not reversible, it is difficult to get the starting materials back again. [ T ]

**②** Circle the **three** non-reversible changes. **(3 marks)**

(burning)  melting  condensing  freezing

(adding vinegar to bicarbonate of soda)  (rusting)

**③** Some children are talking about reversible changes and changes that are not reversible.

**Barney**
Dissolving sugar in tea is a reversible change.

**Kamal**
When you fry an egg, the changes are not reversible.

**Simon**
Making ice from water is not reversible.

**Maya**
Pouring sand into water is not reversible.

Add a tick (✓) or cross (✗) in the table to show whether each person is right or wrong. **(4 marks)**

| Name | Right or wrong? |
|------|-----------------|
| Barney | ~~writing~~ ✗ |
| Kamal | ~~Rhug~~ ✓ |
| Simon | ✗ |
| Maya | ✗ |

Total — 11

## How you see

**1** Tick the **three** light sources. **(3 marks)**

Sun ☑        star ☑

television ☐        mirror ☐

Moon ☑        eyes ☐

**2** You must never look directly at the Sun. Explain why. **(1 mark)**

_Its too bright and will hurt your eyes_

**3** Toby is reading a book with a torch. On the picture, draw one more arrow to show how he sees the book. **(1 mark)**

**4** Circle the correct **bold** word in each pair to explain how you see a flower. **(5 marks)**

If you look at a flower outside, light from the Sun travels **to/⟨from⟩** the flower in a **curved/⟨straight⟩** line. The flower **blocks/⟨reflects⟩** the light. The **blocked/⟨reflected⟩** light travels to your **ear/⟨eye⟩**.

**5** The man is having his hair cut. On the picture, draw one more arrow to show how the hairdresser sees the image of the man's hair in the mirror. Your arrow will cross over one of the arrows that is already there. **(1 mark)**

light

**Parent tip!** Make sure your child uses a ruler to draw straight arrows.

Total — 11

## Shadows

**❶** Look at the photo. Why does a shadow form when sunlight shines on the dog?
Tick the correct answer.

**(1 mark)**

The dog is transparent. ☐

The dog is moving. ☐

The dog is opaque. ☑

The dog is looking at its shadow. ☐

**❷** Circle the opaque materials.　**(2 marks)**

glass　(wood)　(gold)　water

**❸** The shadow in the picture is short. The photo was taken in the middle of the day.

**a.** Explain why the shadow is short.　**(1 mark)**

Because the sun is right above us.

**b.** How would the shadow be different in the evening? Explain your answer.　**(2 marks)**

In the evening the shadow would be longer because the sun is lower in the sky.

 **Parent tip!**

Encourage your child to make shadows on sunny days. Ask them to work out how to change the size of the shadows, and to explain what they see.

Total — 6

## Solar system

**1** What is the shape of the Sun? .................................. **(1 mark)**

**2** Write **T** next to the statements that are true and
**F** next to the statements that are false. **(5 marks)**

**A** The Moon is a planet. ☐

**B** The Moon orbits the Earth. ☐

**C** The Moon's orbit takes 365 days. ☐

**D** There is one moon in our Solar System. ☐

**E** The Moon is crescent-shaped. ☐

**3** Lucy uses the Internet to find out some data about planets.
She writes the data in a table.

| Planet | Distance of planet from Sun (million km) | Time to orbit Sun (Earth years) | Relative mass of planet compared to Earth (mass of Earth = 1) |
|---|---|---|---|
| Mercury | 58 | 0.24 | 0.055 |
| Venus | 108 | 0.62 | 0.815 |
| Earth | 150 | 1.0 | 1.00 |
| Mars | 228 | 1.9 | 0.107 |
| Jupiter | 778 | 12 | 318 |
| Saturn | 1427 | 29 | 95.2 |
| Uranus | 2871 | 84 | 14.4 |
| Neptune | 4498 | 165 | 17.1 |

**a.** List the planets that have a smaller mass than Earth. **(3 marks)**

.................................   .................................   .................................

**b.** Which planet is furthest from the Sun? .................................. **(1 mark)**

**c.** Which planet takes the shortest time to orbit the Sun?

.................................. **(1 mark)**

**d.** Describe the relationship between the distance of the planet from
the Sun and the time to orbit the Sun. **(2 marks)**

.................................................................................................

.................................................................................................

Total $\frac{}{13}$

# Day and night

**❶** Circle the picture that represents the Earth rotating on its axis. **(1 mark)**

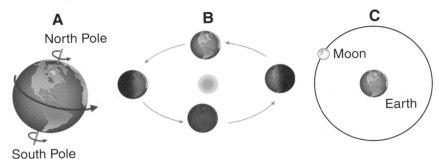

**A**
North Pole

South Pole

**B**

**C**
Moon

Earth

**❷** Tick the box that shows how long it takes for the Earth to
rotate on its axis. **(1 mark)**

1 year ☐    1 week ☐    1 month ☐    1 day ☐

**❸** Tick the box that gives the best scientific answer for
what one day is. **(1 mark)**

From sunrise to sunset ☐

From midday to midnight ☐

From 06:00 one day to 06:00 the next day ☐

From 09:00 to 15:00 ☐

**❹ a.** Use the picture to help you explain why
it is sometimes dark and sometimes light
where you live. **(2 marks)**

.......................................................................................................

.......................................................................................................

.......................................................................................................

**b.** If it is midday at spot A, at which spot would the time be closest
to midnight? ................................... **(1 mark)**

A   C   D

B

Total — 6

## Moving surfaces

**1** Write **T** next to the statements that are true and **F** next to the statements that are false. **(7 marks)**

**A** Pushes and pulls are forces. ☐

**B** Friction tends to speed things up. ☐

**C** Friction is a force. ☐

**D** Friction tends to stop things moving. ☐

**E** Friction is always a nuisance. ☐

**F** Friction acts between surfaces if at least one of the surfaces is moving. ☐

**G** The smoother the surface, the greater the friction. ☐

**2** Reggie is investigating friction.
He measures the force to pull a shoe over three different surfaces.
His results are in the table.

| Surface | Force to pull shoe (N) | | | |
|---|---|---|---|---|
| | **first time** | **second time** | **third time** | **average** |
| carpet | 23 | 20 | 17 | 20 |
| sandpaper | 25 | 25 | 22 | 24 |
| wood | 16 | 19 | 16 | |

**a.** Suggest why Reggie tests each surface three times.

.................................................................................. **(1 mark)**

**b.** Calculate the average force to pull the shoe over the wood. **(2 marks)**

.................................................................................

.................................................................................

**c.** On which surface is the frictional force smallest? Explain how you know. **(2 marks)**

.................................................................................

.................................................................................

**Parent tip!** Scientists repeat tests and calculate average values to improve the accuracy of their results.

Total —— 12

## Gravity and magnets

**❶** Choose from the words below to complete the sentences.

> **non-contact**      **gravity**      **air resistance**
>
> **contact**      **magnetism**

Jake drops his shopping. The force of ............................ pulls it
towards the Earth. The force acts on the shopping even though
it is not touching the shopping. This shows that the force is a

............................ force.                                      **(2 marks)**

**❷** Draw circles around the materials that are magnetic.      **(2 marks)**

       **iron**      **copper**      **steel**      **wood**      **paper**

**❸** The blue object in the picture is a magnet.
How do you think this magnet is useful in
a car scrap yard?      **(1 mark)**

...................................................................................

**❹** How could Natasha use the paperclips to find out which of
these magnets is stronger?

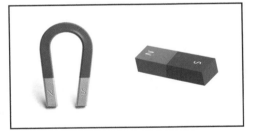
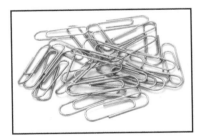

Write detailed instructions of the investigation she could do.      **(3 marks)**

...................................................................................

...................................................................................

...................................................................................

...................................................................................

Total —  8

## Simple machines

**1** Circle the correct **bold** word in each pair. **(2 marks)**

A man uses a crowbar to open a door. A crowbar is a type of
**gear/lever**. The further away from the door he holds the lever,
the **easier/harder** it is for him to open the door.

**2** Give **three** examples of simple machines. **(3 marks)**

.................................................................................................................................

.................................................................................................................................

.................................................................................................................................

**3** Fill in the gaps with the correct words.
Use the picture to help you. **(2 marks)**

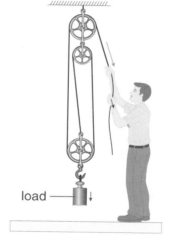

| lever | pulley | less | more |

load

The weight is attached to a ................................. system. The force

needed to lift the load with this system is ................................. than

the force needed to lift the load without this system.

**4** Caitlin attaches a handle to cog wheel **R**.
She uses the handle to turn the cog wheels.

R          S

a. Which cog wheel turns more slowly: **R** or **S**? ................... **(1 mark)**

b. Which cog has the bigger turning force? ................... **(1 mark)**

Total $\frac{}{9}$

# Vibration, volume and pitch

**❶** Draw lines to match each word to its meaning. **(3 marks)**

**Word**

| pitch |
| volume |
| medium |

**Meaning**

| a material that sound travels through |
| how high or low a sound is |
| how loud or soft a sound is |

**❷** Circle the correct **bold** word in each pair. **(2 marks)**

A vibrating object makes a sound. The bigger the vibrations, the **quieter/louder** the sound. As you move away from the source of a sound, the sound appears to get **quieter/louder**.

**❸** Two children make an instrument out of bottles. They talk about their predictions.

**Leo**
When you hit the bottles with a spoon, the bottle with most water will have the lowest pitch.

**Paige**
When you bang the bottles with a spoon, the one with the most water in it will sound loudest.

**a.** Explain why Paige is not correct. **(1 mark)**

...................................................................................................................

...................................................................................................................

**b.** Use ideas about vibrations to explain why Leo is correct. **(1 mark)**

...................................................................................................................

...................................................................................................................

...................................................................................................................

...................................................................................................................

**Total** 7

# Making circuits

**1** Add circuit symbols and words to complete the table. **(6 marks)**

| Component | Circuit symbol |
|---|---|
| cell | ................................................................ |
| ............................................... | (M) |
| bulb | ................................................................ |
| wire | ................................................................ |
| ............................................... | ⊥⊥ (bulb symbol) |
| ............................................... | —o⁄ o— |

**2** Complete the sentences below. **(2 marks)**

In a torch, the electricity flows around a ..................................

Electricity only flows if this is ..................................

**3** Write each material in the correct column of the table. **(9 marks)**

> copper    aluminium    plastic    wood    silver
> paper    cardboard    glass    iron

| Conductors | Insulators |
|---|---|
|  |  |
|  |  |
|  |  |

**4** Explain why the bulb does not light in the circuit below. **(1 mark)**

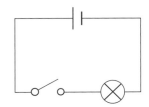

..................................................................................

# Changing circuits

**1** Oscar sets up circuit A with one bulb and one cell.
Then he adds another cell to make circuit B.

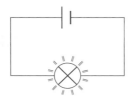

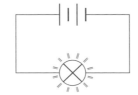

Circuit A                    Circuit B

**a.** Is the bulb brighter in circuit A or circuit B? .................... **(1 mark)**

**b.** Explain your answer to part **a**. **(1 mark)**

.................................................................................................................

.................................................................................................................

**2** Olivia asks a scientific question:
How *does the number of bulbs in a circuit affect their brightness?*

She sets up the circuit below.

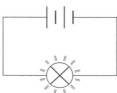

Top tip! To make a test fair, keep all the variables the same except for the variables you are investigating.

She adds two more bulbs and records their brightness in a table.

| .......................... | **Brightness** |
|---|---|
| 1 | most bright |
| 2 | less bright |
| 3 | least bright |

**a.** Write down **one** thing she must do to make the

investigation fair. ................................................................... **(1 mark)**

**b.** Write the missing column heading in the table. **(1 mark)**

**3** Use the results in the table to describe the relationship between the
number of bulbs and their brightness. **(2 marks)**

.................................................................................................................

.................................................................................................................

Total — 6

**1** Alison wants to grow tomato plants in her garden.

**a.** She tests the soil in different parts of her garden. She draws pie charts to display her results.

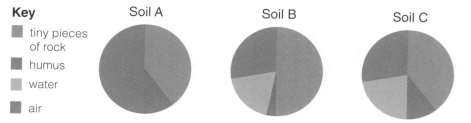

Key
■ tiny pieces of rock
■ humus
■ water
■ air

Soil A    Soil B    Soil C

**i.** Why will the plants not grow well in soil A? **(1 mark)**

.................................................................................................

**ii.** Humus is made up of tiny pieces of dead plants and animals.
Tomato plants grow well in humus-rich soil.
Which soil is best for growing tomatoes: A, B or C? ................... **(1 mark)**

**b.** The diagram shows a tomato plant.

Tick the **two** parts of the plant that support it. **(2 marks)**

roots ☐          flowers ☐

stem ☐           leaves ☐

**c.** Alison notices aphids eating the leaves of her tomato plants.
Here is a food chain that includes aphids.

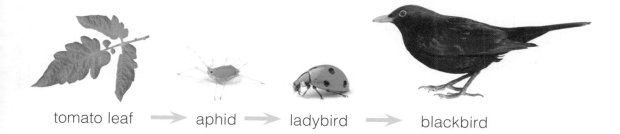

tomato leaf ➔ aphid ➔ ladybird ➔ blackbird

**i.** Name the producer in the food chain. ........................... **(1 mark)**

**ii.** Alison wants ladybirds to come to her garden.
Suggest why. **(1 mark)**

.....................................................................................................

.....................................................................................................

**iii.** Name two predators in the food chain.

........................... and ........................... **(2 marks)**

**d.** The diagram shows a tomato flower.
Fill in the **two** missing labels. **(2 marks)**

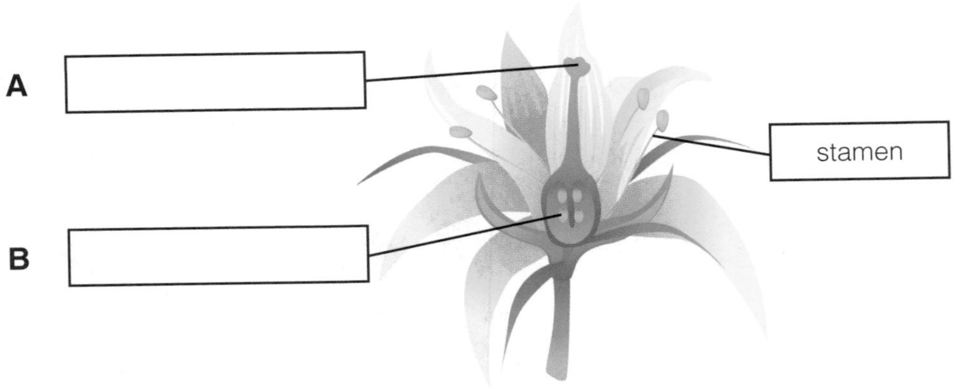

A [                    ]

stamen

B [                    ]

**e.** The steps below describe how the tomato flowers produce seeds, but they are in the wrong order.
Write a number next to each step to show the correct order. The first one has been done for you. **(4 marks)**

| 1 | Pollen travels from the stamen to stigma. |

[  ] This is fertilisation.

[  ] Pollen joins with ovules to make seeds.

[  ] This is pollination.

[  ] Pollen moves down to the ovary.

**f.** The tomatoes grow and Alison eats them. Tomatoes are rich in which type of nutrient? Tick the correct box. **(1 mark)**

carbohydrates [  ]     fats [  ]

protein [  ]     vitamins and minerals [  ]

**2** Roisin is investigating ice. She puts ice cubes on plates.

She uses her watch to measure the time it takes for the ice to melt. Her results are in the table.

| Number of ice cubes | Time to melt (minutes) |
| --- | --- |
| 1 | 128 |
| 2 | 137 |
| 4 | 142 |
| 8 | 163 |

**a.** Describe the relationship between the number of ice cubes and the time it takes for them to melt. **(2 marks)**

....................................................................................................

....................................................................................................

**b.** Describe **one** thing that Roisin should do to make her investigation fair. **(1 mark)**

....................................................................................................

....................................................................................................

**c.** Complete the sentences.

Ice ................................. to make liquid water. If you put the water in the freezer, it will freeze to form ice again.

Ice is water in the ................................. state. **(2 marks)**

**d.** Miss Davies gives Roisin an ice cube with sand mixed up in it. She asks Roisin to give her some dry sand from the mixture at the end of the week.

Write step-by-step instructions to tell Roisin what to do. In your answer, include the names of **two** changes of state and **one** separation technique. **(3 marks)**

....................................................................................................

....................................................................................................

....................................................................................................

....................................................................................................

**3** Afiba lives in Nigeria. One day the Moon comes between the Earth and the Sun. Afiba cannot see the Sun for a few minutes.

**a.** Choosing from the words below, fill in the gaps with the correct words. **(5 marks)**

> star    transparent    planet    **Earth**    **Sun**    opaque    **Moon**

The Sun is a ................................. The Earth is a ................................. The

Earth orbits the ................................. The Moon orbits the .................................

The Moon is .................................

**b.** The red arrows show rays of light from the Sun.

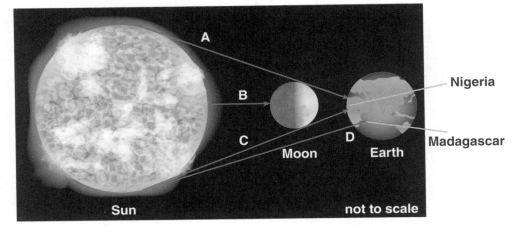

**i.** Use arrow B to explain why there is a shadow of the Moon on the Earth. **(2 marks)**

.................................................................................................................

.................................................................................................................

.................................................................................................................

**ii.** What is the shape of the Moon's shadow on the Earth?

................................................................. **(1 mark)**

**iii.** Haja lives in Madagascar. Use arrow D to explain why he can see the Sun. **(2 marks)**

.................................................................................................................

.................................................................................................................

**iv.** Why must you never look directly at the Sun? **(1 mark)**

.................................................................................................................

## VARIETY OF LIFE

**page 5**
1 Plants make their own food.
2 An animal with a bony skeleton, including a backbone.
3 mammals, birds, fish, amphibians, reptiles
4 insects and spiders
5 worm

**page 7**
1 air, water, nutrients, light, space
2 The flower makes seeds.
3 roots and stem
4 Leaves take in carbon dioxide from the air. They use carbon dioxide and water to make food for the plant.

## GROWING AND CHANGING

**page 9**
1 When an animal changes completely as it grows.
2 **Any reasonable examples**, including butterfly or ladybird (insects) and frog (amphibian).
3 frog spawn, tadpole, froglet, frog
4 egg, larva (caterpillar), pupa (chrysalis), adult butterfly

**page 11**
1 Making a new living thing.
2 one
3 Pollination is the transport of pollen from one flower to another; fertilisation is the joining of pollen with ovules to make seeds.
4 The bird eats the berries. It does not digest the seed, which comes out of its body in its faeces. The seed can then grow.

## YOUR BODY

**page 13**
1 heart, blood and blood vessels
2 pumps blood around the body
3 **Any two from:** nutrients, oxygen, waste substances.
4 Any answer above 150 beats per minute.

**page 15**
1 The structure of bones in a body.
2 support, movement and protection
3 **Any named five animals from these groups:** mammals, birds, fish, amphibians and reptiles.
4 In order to bend your elbow upwards, your biceps muscle contracts. It pulls up the bone it is joined to at the bottom of your arm. At the same time, the other muscle underneath your arm is relaxed.

**page 17**
1 carbohydrates, fats, proteins, vitamins and minerals
2 **Any two foods that are high in fat:** for example, chips, cakes, cheese, butter, oil
3 heart, stomach, brain, liver
4 alcohol and tobacco

**page 19**
1 To break down food so your body can absorb it.
2 Digestive juices start to digest food in the stomach.
3 Avoid sugary food and drinks, brush your teeth twice a day, go to the dentist for check-ups.

4 Incisors are flat and molars are wider with a rough surface. This means that incisors are suitable for biting off pieces of food and molars are suitable for chewing and grinding.

## WEB OF LIFE

**page 21**
1 A living thing that makes its own food; a plant.
2 **a** snail and frog
  **b** frog
3 grass $\longrightarrow$ zebra $\longrightarrow$ lion

**page 23**
1 The surroundings of a plant or animal that supplies everything that the plant or animal needs.
2 The number of foxes will decrease.
3 There is less ice, so it is harder for polar bears to hunt and find prey animals like seals. The distances between ice platforms are greater, making swimming between them more perilous.

**page 25**
1 **Accept any sensible suggestion**, including different-coloured eyes, different-coloured hair, more or fewer freckles, and so on.
2 The eagle has sharp talons for grasping and carrying off its prey, and a sharp beak for catching its prey and tearing its flesh.
3 The plants or animals that are produced by their parent or parents.
4 The development of plants or animals over many years.

## EARTH

**page 27**
1 The preserved remains or traces of an animal or plant that lived many years ago.
2 A rock that water can soak into.
3 tiny pieces of rock, dead plants and dead animals, air and water
4 Crystals, because it is hard and non-porous.

## STATES OF MATTER

**page 29**
1 solid, liquid, gas
2 melting
3 **Accept two from:** The shape of a solid does not change unless you apply a force, but a liquid takes the shape of the bottom of the container it is in. You can hold a solid but you cannot easily hold a liquid. You can pour a liquid but you cannot usually pour a solid.

**page 31**
1 evaporation
2 condensation
3 It will evaporate more quickly in Dar es Salaam
4 Water evaporates from the oceans and other bodies of water. It rises through the atmosphere. High above Earth it condenses to form clouds, then falls as rain for drinking and to water crops, etc.

## MIXING AND MAKING

**page 33**
1 A material that lets light through and that you can see through.
2 **Four from:** Wood is opaque. It is an electrical insulator. It is a thermal insulator. It is not magnetic. It is softer than steel.
3 diamond

## page 35

1 A mixture is made up of two or more materials. It is often easy to separate the materials in a mixture.
2 **Any three from:** melting, freezing, evaporating, condensing, dissolving.
3 evaporation
4 Water can pass through the tiny holes, but sand cannot. This means that sand remains in the filter paper and water passes through into the container below.

## page 37

1 A variable you keep the same in a fair test.
2 burning <u>melting</u> rusting <u>dissolving</u>
3 In a change that is reversible you can get back the original materials; no new materials are made. In a change that is not reversible it is difficult – or impossible – to get the starting materials back again; one or more new materials are made.
4 Not reversible. You cannot get the untoasted bread back again.

## LIGHT

### page 39

1 **Five from this list, or other suitable answers:** Sun, other stars, lamps, torches, candles, computer screens, television.
2 mirror
3

4 $190\,cm - 150\,cm = 40\,cm$

### page 41

1 An area of darkness on a surface caused by an opaque object blocking out light.
2 You can see through a transparent object because light passes through it. You cannot see through an opaque material because light does not pass through it.
3 **One from:** lamp, block of wood, ruler.
4 By moving it closer to the lamp or moving the lamp closer to it.

## SPACE

### page 43

1 Sun
2 Earth
3 **One from:** They are all roughly spherical. They are all part of the same solar system.
4 The Earth orbits the Sun but the Moon orbits the Earth.

### page 45

1 24 hours
2 towards the east
3 When the part of the Earth you are on faces the Sun, it is light. When the part of the Earth you are on faces away from the Sun, it is dark.
4 The Earth moves towards the east, so we see the Sun rise in the east in the morning and set in the west in the evening.

## FORCES

### page 47

1 A force that acts between surfaces and slows down or stops things that are moving.
2 friction, air resistance, water resistance
3 $5N + 7N + 6N = 18N$
  $18N \div 3 = 6N$
4 parachute B

### page 49

1 The force between two objects. It pulls things towards the Earth.
2 copper <u>iron</u> wood <u>steel</u> leather
3 The poles will push each other apart – they will repel each other.
4 She could repeat the investigation with steel nails instead of paper clips.

### page 51

1 A device that changes the direction or size of a force.
2 pulley, gear, lever
3 A screwdriver because you need to apply less force if the lever is longer.

## SOUND

### page 53

1 It must vibrate.
2 **Any three reasonable answers**, including air, water, wood.
3 The sound gets quieter.
4 viola; larger size

## ELECTRICITY

### page 55

1

2 Electricity does not flow through the circuit, so the components do not work.
3 **Conductors – any two correct answers**, including copper and iron; **insulators – any two correct answers**, including wood and plastic.
4 cell or battery

### page 57

1 A component that turns a device on and off.
2 the number of cells
3 The greater the number of cells, the louder the buzzer.
4 The bulb does not light because there is a gap in the circuit, there is no cell/battery and the switch is open/off.

## WORKBOOK

## VARIETY OF LIFE

### page 58

1 snake  shark  (bee)  (spider)
  (ant)  frog  (snail)  bat                    **(4 marks)**
2 There are two big groups of plants: non-flowering plants and **flowering** plants. Non-flowering plants include mosses and **ferns/conifer trees**. Grasses are in the **flowering** plants group.
                                              **(3 marks)**
3 **Accept two from:** feathers, wings, lay eggs.
                                              **(2 marks)**
4 a  fish                                    **(1 mark)**
  b  mammals                                 **(1 mark)**
5 (horse chestnut)                           **(1 mark)**

**page 59**

1 water **(1 mark)**

2 **From left to right:** stem, roots. **(2 marks)**

3 d make food ☑ **(1 mark)**

4 a blue **(1 mark)**

 b colour of food dye **(1 mark)**

 c The stem transports the different-coloured water to the flowers. **(1 mark)** When the different-coloured water reaches the flower, the flower gradually changes colour. **(1 mark)**

## GROWING AND CHANGING

**page 60**

1 child – they learn to walk and talk; baby – they feed on milk from their mother's breasts; adult – they are fully grown; teenager – their body changes rapidly **(4 marks: award 1 mark for each correct match)**

2 bee ☑ **(1 mark)**

 ladybird ☑ **(1 mark)**

3 egg, larva, pupa, adult **(4 marks)**

4 **Clockwise from top right:** frog, frog spawn, tadpole, froglet **(4 marks: award 1 mark for each correct label).**

5 **Include these points:** an adult chicken lays an egg **(1 mark)**. If the female has mated with a male, a chick develops inside the egg **(1 mark)**. After a few weeks, the chick hatches **(1 mark)**. It grows into a chicken **(1 mark)**.

**page 61**

1 a pollination – pollen travels from the stamen of one flower to the stigma of another; fertilisation – pollen joins with ovules to make seeds; dispersal – seeds move away from the plant. **(3 marks: award 1 mark for each correct match)**

 b pollination and dispersal **(2 marks)**

2 a

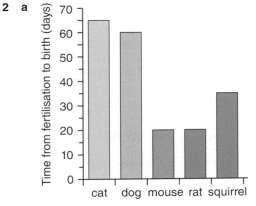

 Mammal
 **(5 marks: award 1 mark for each correct bar)**

 b As the time from fertilisation to birth increases, **the adult animal gets heavier**. **(1 mark)**

## YOUR BODY

**page 62**

1 B **(1 mark)**

2  **(3 marks)**

3 a 80 + 85 + 75 = 240 **(1 mark)**
 240 ÷ 3 = 80 beats per minute **(1 mark)**
 **(Award only 1 mark for correct calculation but wrong answer.)**

 b Rachel **(1 mark)**; her heart rate is much higher than anyone else's **(1 mark)**.

**page 63**

1 bones **(1 mark)**

2 support **(1 mark)**, protection **(1 mark)**, movement **(1 mark)**. **Answers can be in any order.**

3 a B **(1 mark)**

 b A **(1 mark)**

 c to protect the brain **(1 mark)**

4 a **Accept any two reasonable answers, including:** they both have ribs, they both have skulls, they both have bones in their necks, they both have a backbone **(2 marks: award 1 mark for each correct answer)**

 b **Accept any two reasonable answers, including:** the wolf has shorter bones in its neck; the wolf has shorter bones in its legs **(2 marks: award 1 mark for each correct answer)**

**page 64**

1 pasta – carbohydrate; chicken – protein; butter – fat; fruit – vitamins and minerals **(4 marks: award 1 mark for each correct match)**

2 The two nutrients whose main job is to provide you with energy are (carbohydrates) and (fats). The nutrients whose main job is to keep everything working properly are (vitamins) and (minerals). The main nutrient that your body uses to repair damage is (protein). **(5 marks)**

3 A substance that affects how your body works. ☑ **(1 mark)**

4 It can damage their heart. ☑
 It might make them sick. ☑
 It can damage their brain. ☑ **(3 marks)**

**page 65**

1

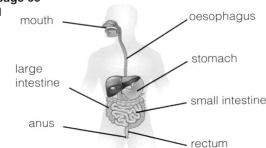

 **(7 marks: award 1 mark for each correct answer)**

2 a Your tongue detects taste and teeth chew food. Saliva starts to break down food. **(1 mark)**

 b Chewed food mixes with digestive juices; food starts to break down. **(1 mark)**

 c Faeces leave your body. **(1 mark)**

3 incisors – bite off pieces of food; canines – tear food such as meat; molars – grind and chew food **(3 marks: award 1 mark for each correct match)**

4 Answer: meat **(1 mark)** Reason: It has huge canines to tear food. **(1 mark)**

## WEB OF LIFE

**page 66**

1  a   is eaten by                                      (1 mark)
   b   lion                                             (1 mark)
   c   grass                                            (1 mark)
   d   wildebeest                                       (1 mark)
2  a   crab                                             (1 mark)
   b   **Accept two from:** the number of limpets
       will increase, the number of seagulls will
       decrease, the amount of seaweed will
       decrease. **(2 marks: award 1 mark for each
       correct reason)**

**page 67**

1  a   pond weed                                        (1 mark)
   b   The number will decrease.                        (1 mark)
   c   They will increase **(1 mark)** because there
       are fewer foxes to eat them.                     (1 mark)
   d   pond weed ⟶ water boatman ⟶
       newt ⟶ hedgehog                                  (1 mark)

**page 68**

1  big size – it stops other animals killing them;
   trunks – they can reach high-up food, and drink
   water from low down; tusks – helps them to strip
   bark from trees to eat, and dig to find water
   under dried-up rivers; big ears – helps them to
   cool down                                            **(4 marks)**
2  1A, 2C, 3B, 4E, 5D        **(4 marks: award 1 mark
                              for each correct answer)**

## EARTH

**page 69**

1  a   A                                                (1 mark)
   b   C                                                (1 mark)
2  a   67 g – 50 g **(1 mark)** = 17 g **(1 mark)**
   b   E **(1 mark)**   c   E **(1 mark)**

## STATES OF MATTER

**page 70**

1  liquid                                               (1 mark)
2  ice                                                  (1 mark)
3  Gas: **yes**, yes; liquid: **no, yes**; solid: no, no
   **(4 marks: award 1 mark for each correct
   answer)**
4  freezing                                             (1 mark)
5  a   iron                                             (1 mark)
   b   1083 °C – 1063 °C = 20 °C **(2 marks: award
       only 1 mark for correct calculation but
       wrong answer)**

**page 71**

1  A – Water **condenses** here.
   B – Water **evaporates** here.                       (2 marks)
2  The Sun (heats) water in the sea. Some water
   (evaporates) to make water vapour. This rises
   and (cools). It (condenses) to make liquid water
   in clouds. Liquid water falls from clouds as
   (rain). **(5 marks: award 1 mark for each correct
   answer)**
3  a   The place he leaves the kitchen roll. **(1 mark)**
   b   By putting the same amount of water on each
       piece of kitchen roll.                           (1 mark)
   c   On top of a heater – dry; in the playground
       (where it is cold and not raining) – wet; on a
       table inside – slightly damp **(3 marks: award
       1 mark for each correct match)**

## MIXING AND MAKING

**page 72**

1  hardness – how easy or difficult it is to scratch;
   thermal conductivity – how well heat travels
   through it; response to magnets – whether it is
   attracted to a magnet; transparency – whether it
   is see-through **(4 marks: award 1 mark for each
   correct match)**

2  It is a good electrical conductor. ☑

   It is bendy. ☑                                       (2 marks)
3  (iron)   wood   gold   (steel)                       (2 marks)
4

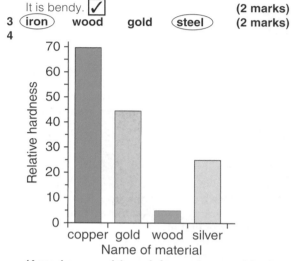

**(4 marks: award 1 mark for each correct bar)**

**page 73**

1  Kassim                                               (1 mark)
2  Put the mixture in a sieve with holes that are
   smaller than the grains of sand but bigger than
   the tiny pieces of flour **(1 mark)**. Move the sieve
   quickly from side to side **(1 mark)**. The flour will
   come through the sieve. You can collect it in a
   container below the sieve **(1 mark)**. The sand will
   remain in the sieve **(1 mark)**.
3  Harriet adds salt to water and stirs. The salt
   **dissolves** to make a **solution**. This shows that
   salt is **soluble** in water. Then she gets another
   cup of water. She adds sand to the water.
   The sand does not **dissolve** in water. It is not
   **soluble**. You can separate sand and water by
   **filtering**. **(6 marks: award 1 mark for each
   correct answer)**

**page 74**

1  A – F, B – F, C – T, D – T        **(4 marks: award
                              1 mark for each correct answer)**

2  (burning)  melting  condensing  freezing

   (adding vinegar to bicarbonate of soda)

   (rusting)                                            (3 marks)
3  Barney: right; Kamal: right; Simon: wrong; Maya:
   wrong.
   **(4 marks: award 1 mark for each correct 'right
   or wrong' answer)**

## LIGHT

**page 75**

1  Sun ☑     star ☑     television ☑
                                                        **(3 marks)**
2  It is very bright and can damage your eyes.
                                                        **(1 mark)**

**3** (1 mark)

**4** If you look at a flower outside, light from the Sun travels (to) the flower in a (straight) line. The flower (reflects) the light. The (reflected) light travels to your (eye). **(5 marks: award 1 mark for each correct answer)**

**5** (1 mark)

### page 76

**1** The dog is opaque. ☑ (1 mark)

**2** glass (wood) (gold) water (2 marks)

**3 a** The Sun is high in the sky, it is overhead. (1 mark)

**b** The shadow would be longer **(1 mark)** because the Sun is lower in the sky **(1 mark)**.

## SPACE

### page 77

**1** spherical **(1 mark)**

**2** A – F, B – T, C – F, D – F, E – F **(5 marks: award 1 mark for each correct answer)**

**3 a** Mercury **(1 mark)**, Venus **(1 mark)**, Mars **(1 mark)**

**b** Neptune (1 mark)

**c** Mercury (1 mark)

**d** As the distance of the planet from the Sun increases **(1 mark)**, the time to orbit the Sun increases **(1 mark)**.

### page 78

**1** **A** should be circled (1 mark)

**2** 1 day ☑ (1 mark)

**3** From 06:00 one day to 06:00 the next day ☑ (1 mark)

**4 a** When you are in the half of the Earth that is facing the Sun, it is light **(1 mark)**.
When the Earth rotates and you are in the half of the Earth that is not facing the Sun, it is dark **(1 mark)**.

**b** D (1 mark)

## FORCES

### page 79

**1** A – T, B – F, C – T, D – T, E – F, F – T, G – F **(7 marks: award 1 mark for each correct answer)**

**2 a** to improve the accuracy of his results (1 mark)

**b** 16 N + 19 N + 16 N = 51 N (1 mark)
51 N ÷ 3 = 17 N (1 mark)

**c** The frictional force is smallest on the wood **(1 mark)**, where the force to pull the shoe is smallest at only 17 N **(1 mark)**.

### page 80

**1** Jake drops his shopping. The force of **gravity** pulls it towards the Earth. The force acts on the shopping even though it is not touching the shopping. This shows that the force is a **non-contact** force. (2 marks)

**2** (iron) copper (steel) wood paper (2 marks)

**3** It separates iron and steel objects from objects made out of other materials. (1 mark)

**4** Add paper clips, in a line, to each magnet in turn **(1 mark)**. Count the number of paper clips that each magnet can hold **(1 mark)**. The one that can hold more paper clips is stronger **(1 mark)**.

### page 81

**1** A man uses a crowbar to open a door. A crowbar is a type of (lever). The further away from the door he holds the lever, the (easier) it is for him to open the door. **(2 marks)**

**2** pulleys **(1 mark)**, levers **(1 mark)**, gears **(1 mark)**

**3** The weight is attached to a **pulley** system. The force needed to lift the load with this system is **less** than the force needed to lift the load without this system. (2 marks)

**4 a** R (1 mark)

**b** R (1 mark)

## SOUND

### page 82

**1** pitch – how high or low a sound is; volume – how loud or soft a sound is; medium – a material that sound travels through **(3 marks: award 1 mark for each correct match)**

**2** A vibrating object makes a sound. The bigger the vibrations, the (louder) the sound. As you move away from the source of a sound, the sound appears to get (quieter). (2 marks)

**3 a** The amount of water in the bottle affects the pitch of the sound, not its loudness. (1 mark)

**b** Leo is correct because when you hit the bottles with the spoon, the water and the glass vibrates. The more water, the lower the pitch. (1 mark)

## ELECTRICITY

### page 83

**1** cell: ⊣⊢; **motor**: Ⓜ; **bulb**: ⊗;
wire: ────; **buzzer**: ⌓;
switch (open): ──o o──
**(6 marks: award 1 mark for each correct symbol/word)**

**2** In a torch, the electricity flows around a **circuit**. Electricity only flows if this is **complete**. **(2 marks)**

**3** **Conductors:** copper, aluminium, silver, iron.
**Insulators:** plastic, wood, paper, cardboard, glass. **(9 marks: award 1 mark for each correct answer)**

**4** The switch is off/open. (1 mark)

### page 84

**1 a** circuit B (1 mark)

**b** Circuit B has more cells, so there is a greater 'push' to make the electricity go around the circuit. (1 mark)

**2 a** keep the same cells in the circuit **(1 mark)**
  **b** number of bulbs **(1 mark)**
**3** As the number of bulbs increases **(1 mark)**, their brightness decreases **(1 mark)**.

## MIXED PRACTICE QUESTIONS
### pages 85–88

**1 a i** There is no water in the soil. **(1 mark)**
   **ii** C **(1 mark)**

  **b** roots ☑   stem ☑ **(2 marks)**

  **c i** tomato leaf **(1 mark)**
   **ii** To remove the aphids, or reduce their number, by eating them. **(1 mark)**
   **iii** ladybird **(1 mark)**, blackbird **(1 mark)**
  **d** A: stigma
   B: ovule **(2 marks)**
  **e** **2** – This is pollination. **3** – Pollen moves down to the ovary. **4** – Pollen joins with ovules to make seeds. **5** – This is fertilisation.
   **(4 marks)**

  **f** vitamins and minerals ☑ **(1 mark)**

**2 a** As the number of ice cubes increase **(1 mark)**, the time taken to melt increases **(1 mark)**.
  **b** The plates should all be in the same part of the room so that the temperature is the same.
   **(1 mark)**

  **c** Ice **melts** to make liquid water. If you put the water in the freezer, it will freeze to form ice again. Ice is water in the **solid** state. **(2 marks)**
  **d** Allow the ice to **melt** (change of state) **(1 mark)**. **Filter** (separation technique) the sandy mixture **(1 mark)**. Place the damp sand in a warm place so the water can **evaporate** (change of state) from it **(1 mark)**.

**3 a** The Sun is a **star**. The Earth is a **planet**. The Earth orbits the **Sun**. The Moon orbits the **Earth**. The Moon is **opaque**. **(5 marks)**
  **b i** Arrow B shows light from the Sun reaching the Moon, but it can travel no further because the Moon is opaque **(1 mark)**. This light does not reach the Earth **(1 mark)**.
   **ii** round / circular **(1 mark)**
   **iii** Arrow D shows light from the Sun reaching the Earth at Madagascar **(1 mark)**. It is not blocked by an opaque object **(1 mark)**. This is why Haja can see the Sun.
   **iv** You can damage your eyesight. **(1 mark)**

**Adaptations** – The features of an animal or plant that help it to survive in its environment
**Air resistance** – A force that slows things down in air
**Asexual reproduction** – Making a new plant without seeds
**Axis** – An imaginary line between the North Pole and the South Pole, going through the centre of the Earth
**Blood** – Blood is mainly water with dissolved nutrients. It also includes red blood cells
**Blood vessels** – The tubes that blood flows through
**Carbohydrates** – Nutrients that provide energy
**Cell** – A cell pushes electricity around a complete circuit
**Circuit** – Electricity flows around a complete circuit
**Circulatory system** – The circulatory system includes the heart, blood vessels and blood. It transports nutrients and oxygen around the body
**Classification key** – A series of questions to help you identify a living thing
**Classify** – To sort living things into groups depending on their similarities and differences
**Conclusion** – What you have found out in an investigation
**Condense** – The change of state from gas to liquid
**Conductivity** – How easy it is for electricity or heat to travel through a material. The higher the value for electrical conductivity of a material, the more easily electricity travels through it

**Conductor** – A substance that electricity can flow through
**Contract** – When a muscle contracts, it becomes short and fat
**Control variables** – The variables you keep the same in a fair test
**Crystal** – A piece of solid material with a regular shape and flat faces
**Digestive system** – Your digestive system breaks down food so that your body can use it
**Dissolving** – Mixing a solid with a liquid to make a solution
**Drugs** – Substances that affect how your body works
**Electrical insulator** – A substance that electricity cannot flow through
**Environment** – The surroundings of a plant or animal. It supplies everything the plant or animal needs
**Evaporate** – The change of state from liquid to gas
**Evolution** – The development of plants or animals over many years
**Fair test** – An investigation where you keep all the variables the same except the ones that you are changing and measuring
**Fats** – Nutrients that provide energy. Your body can store them
**Fertilisation** – The joining of pollen with ovules to make seeds in plants, or the joining of a sperm with an egg in animals
**Food chain** – A diagram that shows what eats what

**Forces** – Forces can change the movement and shapes of objects

**Fossil** – The preserved remains or traces of an animal or plant that lived many years ago

**Freezing** – The change of state from liquid to solid

**Friction** – A force that acts between surfaces and slows down or stops things that are moving

**Gear system** – A system of cogs that allows a small turning force to have a greater effect

**Grain** – A small piece of a solid material that does not have a regular shape

**Gravity** – The force between two objects. It pulls things towards the Earth

**Hardness** – How easy it is to scratch a material. A hard material is difficult to scratch

**Heart** – The heart pumps blood around the body

**Invertebrate** – An animal without a backbone

**Large intestine** – Water from undigested food passes into the body from here

**Larva** – The young of an animal that hatches from an egg. It is very different from the adult

**Lever** – A straight rod with a pivot. You can use it to exert a big force over a small distance at one end by exerting a smaller force over a bigger distance at the other end

**Light source** – An object that makes light

**Magnetic force** – The force between two magnets, or between a magnet and a magnetic material

**Magnetic material** – A material that is attracted to a magnet

**Medium** – A material that sound travels through. A medium can be in the solid, liquid or gas state

**Melting** – The change of state from solid to liquid

**Metamorphosis** – When an animal changes completely as it grows

**Mixture** – A mixture is made up of two or more materials. It is often easy to separate the materials in a mixture

**Moon** – A natural object that orbits a planet

**Muscles** – Muscles help animals to move

**Not reversible** – A change that is not reversible makes new materials. It is difficult – or impossible – to get the starting materials back again

**Nutrient** – A substance that a plant or animal needs to survive, grow and stay healthy

**Oesophagus** – Chewed food passes down this tube from the mouth to the stomach

**Offspring** – The plants or animals that are produced by their parent or parents

**Opaque** – Light cannot travel through an opaque object

**Orbit** – The circular (or elliptical) path an object in space takes around another object in space

**Pitch** – How high or low a sound is

**Planet** – A big object that orbits a star

**Pollination** – The transport of pollen from one flower to another

**Porous** – Water can soak into a porous material

**Predator** – An animal that eats other animals

**Prediction** – What you expect to happen in an investigation, based on something you already know or have observed

**Prey** – An animal that is eaten by other animals

**Producer** – A living thing that makes its own food. Plants are producers

**Proteins** – Nutrients needed for growth and repair

**Puberty** – The stage of life when a child's body matures to become an adult

**Pulley** – A system of wheels and ropes that make it easier to lift things

**Pupa** – The third stage in the life cycle of some insects

**Reflect** – Light is reflected when it bounces off a surface

**Relax** – When a muscle relaxes, it returns to its original shape

**Repel** – Push away

**Reversible change** – A change in which you can get the original materials back. New substances are not made

**Sexual reproduction** – Making a new living thing by joining pollen with an ovule (in plants) or a sperm with an egg (in animals)

**Shadow** – An area of darkness on a surface caused by an opaque object blocking out light

**Simple machine** – A device that changes the direction or size of a force

**Skeleton** – The structure of bones in a body

**Small intestine** – Digested food passes into the blood from here

**Solar system** – The Sun, and the planets and other objects that orbit it

**Soluble** – A material is soluble if it dissolves in water

**Solution** – A mixture of a solid with a liquid. You cannot see pieces of solid in a solution

**States of matter** – The three forms that matter exists in – solid, liquid and gas

**Stomach** – Digestive juices start to digest food here

**Sun** – The star at the centre of our solar system

**Switch** – A component that turns a device on and off

**Transparency** – A substance is transparent if it lets light through

**Variable** – Something you can change, measure or keep the same in an investigation

**Variation** – The differences between animals or plants of the same type

**Vertebrate** – An animal with a bony skeleton and backbone

**Vibrating** – An object is vibrating if it is moving backwards and forwards again and again

**Vitamins and minerals** – Nutrients that keep your body working properly

**Volume** – The loudness or quietness of a sound

**Voltage** – The 'push' that makes electricity flow around a circuit

**Water cycle** – The journey water takes as it circulates from rivers, lakes and seas to the sky and back again

**Water resistance** – A force that slows things down in water

# Index